MARINE ANIMALS

OF

THE SOUTH WEST

2nd edition

PAUL NAYLOR

This book is dedicated to my son, Samuel, and my mother, Nathalie, with joy that they met.

Acknowledgements

I am indebted to Steve Carpenter for his continued support; to my wife, Teresa, for her unfailing encouragement and positive ideas; and to Emily and Ellie for giving me inspiration. Grateful thanks also go to Alan Hodgson for providing drawings and Seb Shimeld, Anne-Marie Coriat, Ann Beeby and Tom Alderson for finding time in their busy schedules to comment so constructively on the text. I should also thank everyone who made the first edition a success, thus making this book possible. Finally, acknowledgements go to the animals themselves, for their patience when faced by my flashguns and voyeurism.

The author

Paul Naylor has been watching and photographing the marine animals of the South West of England for much of the last twenty years. Occasional visits to more exotic diving locations have done nothing to dissuade him from the view that West Country marine life is as fascinating as that found anywhere else in the world. Paul gained a doctorate in marine biology while researching into the effects of pollution on shellfish living in the South West's estuaries. He writes regularly about marine life for British diving publications; and gives talks to conservation societies, colleges, schools and diving clubs on the wonders of our marine fauna.

Published by
SOUND DIVING
PUBLICATIONS

First Published 2000

Copyright: Paul Naylor

ISBN 0 9522831 3 1

Sales or other enquiries: phone 07041 351307 (local rate)

Printed by Deltor 01752 841717

CONTENTS

Cover photographs:
Front: Cuttlefish (main),
nudibranch sea slug, male cuckoo wrasse, jewel anemones.
Rear: Tompot blenny, spiny starfish, nudibranch sea slug, lobster.

A diver enjoys a colourful patchwork of jewel anemones at the Eddystone Reef, off Plymouth

Chapter 1
INTRODUCTION

The sea contains the most incredible array of animal life, and the creatures that live in the coastal waters of the South West of England are as varied and fascinating as those found anywhere in the world. Members of every major animal group live here, some in great profusion, and there are many beautiful and intriguing species. I have been snorkelling and diving off the coasts of Dorset, Devon and Cornwall for twenty years and my fascination for their marine inhabitants has grown throughout that time. This book has been written in an attempt to share my enthusiasm.

It is intended that this book will enthrall anyone who loves the sea and help divers and snorkellers to identify many of the animals that they meet. I have written this second edition however, even more in the hope that it will go beyond an identification guide, introducing readers to the fascinating characteristics of different animals and displaying aspects of their varied lifestyles. Identification is a means to an end as well as an end in itself, and discovering how or why an animal behaves as it does can be more interesting than finding out what it is called.

The animal life in West Country waters can not be described as unique, because there are no firm boundaries in the sea, but it certainly has a distinctive character. A number of southerly species are at the northern extent of their range here and so are not found elsewhere in the UK, while some more northern species are relatively rare.

A great advantage of the South West is that it combines some of the very best diving and snorkelling in the UK with very good accessibility. It is therefore easy to become familiar with certain dive sites and their inhabitants. In terms of animal life, familiarity does certainly not breed contempt. If, when diving on a far-away coral reef, I see an exotic fish doing something strange, I don't have any terms of reference. That fish may be doing the same thing every day of every year. If, while diving off Weymouth, I see a common type of crab behaving strangely, it means so much more because I have greater experience on which to base my observations. Seeing a new species is also more exciting in familiar surroundings; is it passing through, has it moved here because of changes in currents or weather, or have I simply been unlucky or unobservant in the past?

It is unfortunately true that marine life in the South West, like that everywhere in the world, is under pressure from a variety of environmental threats. I hope this book does a little to show how much there is that must be conserved.

Seaweed dominates the scenery in a shallow rocky bay

Scenery dominated by suspension-feeding animals on a current-swept reef in deeper water

Where to see the South West's marine animals

Whether snorkelling from a crowded holiday beach at Lulworth or diving on the more remote Manacles reef near the Lizard Peninsula, there will always be plenty of animals to see. Many of the species described here can even be seen while exploring rockpools, particularly those lower down on the shore, although animals that are mainly restricted to the sea shore have generally been omitted from the book. No dive is a "write-off" in terms of creature-watching: the most desolate looking sandy sea bed houses all sorts of highly specialised animals, even though they may be less obvious and colourful than their relatives on the rocky pinnacle or shipwreck you have just managed to miss! The joys of shallow diving from the shore are often overlooked but it provides superb opportunities for settling down and watching or photographing marine life. Long dives are possible without the time-consuming tasks associated with boat preparation and maintenance. However a deeper dive, undertaken with the main objective of exploring a wreck, is also a great opportunity to see a wide range of different animals. Wrecks can be fabulously rich habitats, providing shelter for animals that like to hide away (crabs, lobsters, some fish) and an elevated anchorage for those that rely on filtering material from seawater to gain their food (sea anemones, corals, fan worms).

The animals seen on a dive will vary with the time of year, the time of day and even the roughness of the sea, but the water depth and type of habitat will have the most profound effect. Some animal species will be found only in very particular locations, while others will be encountered virtually every time you put your head underwater. Two examples of very different habitats are shown in the photographs on the opposite page. The top photograph was taken in a typical shallow rocky bay near Plymouth. In such brightly-lit conditions, the scenery is dominated by seaweed. In this case it is mainly thong weed, *Himanthalia elongata*. A few snakelocks anemones are visible on the rocks, this being an unusual sun-seeking anemone species (see page 20). The bottom photograph was taken in deeper water (12 metres) on a current-swept, silt-covered reef in Torbay. There is insufficient light and poor conditions for much seaweed growth, and the scenery is dominated by animals which feed on suspended food swept in by the tidal currents. Such animals include plumose anemones (page 22), feather stars (page 98) and boring sponges (page 12). A few dead men's fingers (page 34) can be spotted, and there is also a "turf" of less prominent encrusting animals.

Using the book

It is very difficult to draw up rules for identifying animals. Key features in one group may be irrelevant in another. The best option is probably to scan through the photographs looking for similar creatures to the one seen, and then refer to the text for more detail. Colour, size and the habitat where found can all give clues to an animal's identity but can also mislead. Information on colour and habitat is given as appropriate, while an idea of approximate size is given for all species in an attempt to put the photographs into perspective. The size given for each species is very much a maximum so the majority of individuals seen may be considerably smaller. It is also possible, however, that the occasional specimen is even larger. The reader may find the number of descriptions preceded by "often", "usually" and "commonly" frustrating but omitting these words would give a false idea of precision and certainty.

A rich variety of animals, living cheek by jowl, in Plymouth Sound

A book such as this cannot hope to be comprehensive in the animal species it covers. Books that deal with just sea slugs or crabs of the UK for example, are about as thick as this one, and such texts should be consulted for more thorough identification. I have tried to include the most frequently seen and obvious animals, while providing a selection from each group that gives an idea of the types of creatures they contain. More familiar animals are covered in more detail. The sections on fish, starfish and crabs, for instance, are more wide-ranging (though still far from exhaustive) than those on sponges and sea squirts. In any case, I have deliberately taken up space to show common animals (velvet swimming crabs, cuttlefish for example) going about their lives, in preference to including less familiar animals sitting still.

Animal classification

There is a complicated scientific classification system for living things but I have tried to refer to this as little as possible. However, the term "phylum" (plural: "phyla") will keep cropping up. A phylum is the broadest sub-division of the animal kingdom. Phyla make useful categories and it is these that have formed, roughly speaking, the remaining chapters of this book. I say roughly, because animals from more than one phylum are described as worms (Chapter 4) while sea squirts (Chapter 8) and fish (Chapter 9) belong to the same phylum. Further subdivisions of phyla are discussed in the relevant chapters. Out of all the animals in this book, only the fish have a proper backbone and are classified as vertebrates. All the rest are invertebrates. A huge array of animal species, from many different groups, can be seen in a small area. The photograph from Plymouth Sound above, for example, shows orange encrusting sponge (Chapter 2), jewel anemones (Chapter 3), coral worms (Chapter 4), top-shells (Chapter 6), star sea squirts (Chapter 8) and a pollack and goldsinny (Chapter 9) all in close proximity. Only representatives from Chapters 5 and 7 are missing, but the odd crab and brittle star are bound to be hiding somewhere!

Latin terms have been kept to an absolute minimum in the book, apart from including the Latin name for individual animal species. Latin species names are undoubtedly useful, partly because many common animals (various sponges, sea anemones, sea slugs and sea squirts for example) have no English name. Latin names are also unambiguous and precise but it should be noted that they are not always constant. The velvet swimming crab has had four different Latin names over the last thirty years, while still being called the velvet swimming crab. A Latin name comes in two parts: the first part denotes the genus (the narrowest classification sub-division before species) and the second the species. Very similar animals may belong to the same genus, in which case they will have the same first name. Totally different animals may have the same second name because it can simply mean "common" or "red" for example. The combination of the two refers to a single species and gives an animal a unique label. The Latin name of the cuckoo wrasse, for example, is *Labrus bimaculatus* and the closely related ballan wrasse, *Labrus bergylta*, belongs to the same genus. Both halves of a Latin name should always be in italics.

Photography

Virtually all the photographs in this book were taken underwater, portraying animals in their natural habitat. Aside from the obvious cases of the cuttlebone and discarded crab moults, the only exceptions are the sea anemone feeding (page 16) and

the little cuttle (page 85) and the rock goby (page 132), which were taken in an aquarium. The great majority of photographs are from the South West but a few species seem to have very shy or uncooperative representatives in our region, so ten photographs are from elsewhere in British waters. Underwater sightings of angler fish, for example, are quite frequent in the West Country, but none have been as photogenic as the individual I encountered near Sunderland (page 110).

All the photographs were taken on Fuji Velvia slide film. I use a Nikon 801 land camera, with a 60 mm (macro) or 20 mm lens, in a dedicated aluminium housing from Subal. Lighting is by electronic flashguns from Sea and Sea, either a single large one (YS300) or two small ones (YS50). A few shots in the book were taken with a Nikonos III, 15 mm lens and single flashgun. I would recommend all the above items for their excellent reliability and performance over many years of hard use. There are many alternatives, however, and any underwater camera system that includes a close-up attachment of some kind and a flashgun can take good photographs of marine life. Without a close-up attachment, you are limited to large subjects in very clear water and without a flash gun, pictures can only be taken in very shallow water. A self-contained underwater camera such as the Nikonos, which relies on a probe for framing and focusing of close-ups, is ideal for photographing static or slow-moving animals such as sea anemones and starfish. However for fish, particularly if they are shy or fast-moving, a single lens reflex (SLR) land camera in a waterproof housing really comes into its own. This type of system is particularly versatile when used with a macro lens, because subjects ranging from tiny sea slugs to large fish can be photographed on the same dive.

Chapter 2
SPONGES

Simple creatures

Apart from minute creatures that consist of a single cell, like amoeba, sponges are the simplest members of the animal kingdom. Their cells are specialised for different functions, such as feeding, support or reproduction, but they do not form complex structures like the cells of higher animals. There are no digestive, nervous or circulatory systems for example. The lack of sophistication in sponges has been demonstrated by famous experiments where, having been broken down by being pushed through fine silk, they soon succeed in reassembling themselves. Because sponges are completely static, they were at one time thought to be plants.

Living filters

Sponges are effectively animated filters and their phylum name, Porifera, means "pore bearer". Water is drawn into the sponge's central cavity through its pores, the numerous tiny holes all over its body surface, and leaves by the outlet vents which are much larger, more obvious and fewer in number than the inlet pores. Special cells within the sponge create the water current with continuously beating cilia (tiny whip-like hairs), and collect suspended food particles that are sucked in. This mechanism is simple but effective, and a sponge only a few centimetres across can filter over 20 litres of seawater in a day.

Reproduction

Sponges can reproduce by asexual processes such as budding, or by sexual means. Most sponges are hermaphrodite (simultaneously male and female) but eggs and sperm from the same sponge mature at different times so it does not fertilise itself. Sperm leaves with the outgoing water current, drifts off to fertilise the eggs in other sponges and free-swimming larvae are produced. The larvae then settle and, if the habitat is right, grow into new sponges.

Support and defence

Sponges are supported by a rudimentary skeleton composed of spicules, protein fibres or both. The spicules are needle-like or branched spiky structures made from calcium or silicon compounds. In tropical sponges, it is their fibrous skeleton that produces a traditional bath sponge when the other constituents are stripped away. In addition to providing support, the sharp spicules help to make sponges unpalatable. Many species also produce unpleasant tasting chemicals to deter predators, as any other escape response is beyond their capabilities.

Sea orange - *Suberites ficus*

Also known as the sulphur sponge, the sea orange is a classic example of the archetypal sponge. It forms quite large rounded masses that have an even but slightly rough surface, which represents the vast number of tiny pores through which water is pumped into the sponge. In every mass, there is at least one large circular opening through which water is pumped out again. It is easy to peer into one of these openings and see something of the sponge's internal structure. Colour is usually orange but can be brownish or yellow. The sea orange is most common on rocks and stones where there is some mud present, and can also be found growing on the shells inhabited by hermit crabs. Here, it may completely enclose the hermit's shell and, if this eventually dissolves, the sponge will form the crab's replacement home. [Up to 20 cm across]

Boring sponge - *Cliona celata*

An obvious mass of the yellow sponge.

The name of this sponge arises, not from its uninteresting nature, but from the fact that it bores its way into soft rock such as that of limestone reefs. In many instances, most of the sponge is hidden within a network of passages and chambers that it has excavated in the substrate. All that is visible on the sea bed are then the characteristic yellow "studs" and vents (see smaller photograph) where water enters and leaves the sponge respectively. Sometimes, however, the sponge outgrows its chambers and can

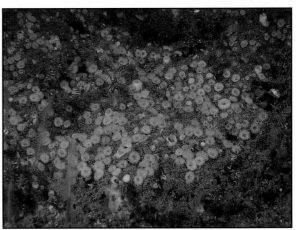

Here, only the vents are visible

form large, very obvious masses, which are still covered in the familiar "studs" and vents. The main photograph shows such a mass, surrounded by trumpet anemones (page 24). The boring process is chemical, and employs an acid by-product of respiration. Special cells use this process to undercut and surround tiny pieces of rock which are then "spat out" with the water flow. The sponge also bores into the shells of molluscs and can be a serious pest in commercial oyster beds. [Masses can reach up to 1 m across but are usually much smaller]

Axinella dissimilis

This distinctive sponge is usually found in quite deep and clear water offshore. Its orange or yellow fan-like form stands erect from rock faces. The branches, which may be joined for part of their length, are flattened and therefore oval in cross-section, with rounded ends. The overall shape is slightly reminiscent of the sea fan (page 36). While totally different types of animal, their form presumably serves the same function in both cases: to maximise the surface area that comes into contact with food-bearing currents. [Up to 15 cm tall]

Breadcrumb sponge - *Halichondria panicea*

A very common encrusting sponge that can form large sheets or lumps on rocks in shallow water, often beneath overhangs. The sheets may be thin or quite thick, with the raised water outlet holes looking like miniature volcanoes or chimneys. It can occur in a variety of shades, from olive green through a dirty cream to pale yellow. The green colouration is due to algae which live symbiotically within the sponge's tissues, and are dependent on the amount of light available. Breadcrumb sponge found under gloomy overhangs or in deeper water has less algae and is therefore more yellow. [Encrustations can reach over 1 m across and are of very variable thickness]

Haliclona oculata

This sponge forms characteristic shrub-like colonies which can grow upwards from a flat sea bed or stick out from a vertical rock surface. The branches, which are often numerous, are dirty yellow or beige in colour, have a round cross-section and bear distinct water outlet holes along their length. *Haliclona* can tolerate quite silty conditions and is common in the outer reaches of estuaries. The fish in this photograph, and the one below, are goldsinny wrasse. ["Shrubs" can be up to 30 cm tall, branches 1 cm across]

Esperiopsis fucorum

Esperiopsis is an encrusting sponge that can form sheets or mounds. It is usually deep orange in colour, and has a delicate, quite flexible consistency. Under more sheltered conditions, it forms many distinctive long and slender tassels that stick out from the rest of the encrustation.

The large water outlet holes may be scattered over a flat surface of the sponge or raised up like chimneys. It grows with great abundance in Plymouth Sound, and dominates the scenery in some areas. [Encrustations of very variable size, tassels can be 10 cm long]

Elephant's hide sponge - *Pachymatisma johnstonia*

The large grey mounds or plates formed by the elephant's hide sponge (sometimes known as the elephant's ear sponge) are usually found protruding from vertical rock faces. Its surfaces are smooth and hard with obvious holes arranged in patches or lines, where water that has passed through the sponge is expelled. Water is taken in through more numerous and much smaller openings all over the body of the sponge. This type of sponges may sometimes be coloured white or blue. The tompot blenny on page 128 is sitting on a growth of this sponge. [Plates can be over 1 m across but usually smaller]

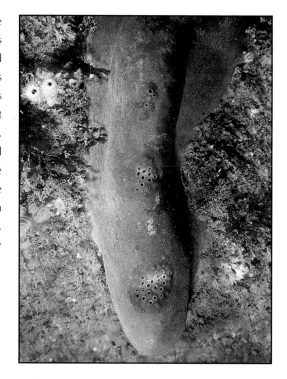

Scypha ciliata

This sponge has a roughly cylindrical shape, rather like a tall, slim vase. The dense cream or brown coloured hairs that cover it produce a distinctive shaggy appearance. It can be found attached to rocks or seaweed, often in small groups. The single water outlet hole is positioned at the free end of the sponge and is surrounded by a ring of longer, stiff hairs. This sponge's body wall is supported by calcium-based spicules and is classified in a different group from all the other species in this chapter, which have silicon-based spicules. [Up to 4 cm long]

Chapter 3
CNIDARIANS
Sea anemones, corals, hydroids & jellyfish

Armed and dangerous

The distinguishing feature of all the animals in this chapter is their possession of stinging cells. These cells contain discharge capsules, also called cnidae, that give the group its name. The discharge capsules, used for both defence and the capture of prey, are impressive examples of engineering in miniature. Each capsule contains a long hollow, coiled thread which uncoils and shoots out under water pressure when the cell is triggered by touch or chemical stimulus. This is achieved by part of the capsule turning itself inside-out (see diagram below). Different threads have varied functions and, when thousands are triggered together, they can have a powerful effect. Some simply entangle the prey, while others stick to it or inject poison. Some even have blades that, in combination with the twisting action of the threads, act as tiny drills on the armoured surfaces of small crustaceans.

A discharge capsule (cnida) before and after discharge.

A step up from sponges

Apart from their exceptional weapon system, cnidarians are fairly simple animals. They have different tissues specialised for various functions, so they are a step up from the sponges, but they do not have proper organs like higher invertebrates. There is no true circulation system and only an extremely simple nerve network. Their tentacles, covered in dense batteries of stinging cells, capture prey animals and pass them to the central mouth where they are engulfed - see photographs below, of a beadlet anemone swallowing a shrimp that it has caught. There is no anus so the mouth is also used for the expulsion of undigested material.

The beadlet anemone at the top is consuming a shrimp

Polyps and medusae - their roles in the different groups

Cnidarians can occur in either the form of a polyp, living anchored to the sea bed, or a free-swimming medusa.

Sea anemones only occur in the polyp form. These flower-like animals are almost always found attached to rocks or other hard surfaces. Water pressure inside the body maintains the anemone's shape and provides a base for muscle action. They reproduce by producing eggs which normally develop into new adults via a planktonic larval stage. Asexual reproduction may also occur, where an adult anemone splits or buds to form a new individual and dense colonies can result.

The following terms are often used when describing sea anemones:

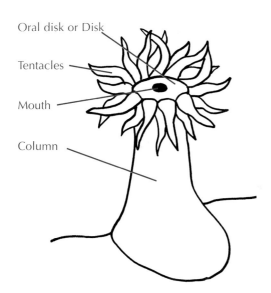

Oral disk or Disk

Tentacles

Mouth

Column

Corals are essentially the same type of animal as sea anemones, occurring only in the polyp form, but they produce some sort of skeleton to support and protect their bodies. Stony corals are usually colonial, their fused skeletons able to form huge coral reefs, but some are completely solitary. Soft corals and sea fans are colonial animals whose "mutual" skeleton is not a solid mass of calcium carbonate, but is gelatinous with embedded calcareous spicules imparting strength and some rigidity

Hydroids, or sea-firs, are the simplest of the stinging-celled animals. Most hydroid species occur in both the polyp and medusa form at different times during their life cycle, but the polyp stage is dominant. The medusa stage may be free swimming or be simply an extension to the polyps. The polyps form colonies where they are linked by strands of living tissue and individuals may serve different functions within the colony. Some polyps, for example, are responsible for feeding while others form the reproductive medusae.

Jellyfish are like hydroids, in usually having both polyp and medusa stages, but it is the medusa stage that dominates as a large floating predator. Its body typically forms a "bell" or "umbrella" which can contract rhythmically to propel the animal through the water. The polyp stage often goes unnoticed or may even be absent altogether. As in all cnidarians, tentacles armed with stinging cells catch prey and pass it to the mouth, so jellyfish can be visualised as floating sea anemones.

Beadlet anemone - *Actinia equina*

The beadlet anemone is usually only seen in very shallow water. Underwater, its dense mass of tapering tentacles can be fully appreciated but when exposed to air between the tidemarks it retracts to resemble a blob of jelly. It is often seen in rock pools. The anemone's column is smooth but the small blue bulges, known as tubercles or acrorhagi, that form a ring just below the tentacles may be visible. Beadlet anemones are most often coloured a deep red but can be green, brown or orange. Unusually for a sea anemone, this species broods its young. [Up to 5 cm across]

Strawberry anemone - *Actinia fragacea*

The column of this dark red anemone bears characteristic bright green spots, so the derivation of its name is obvious. The strawberry anemone has a very similar shape and form to the beadlet anemone but is larger than its close relative and is found in slightly deeper water. For a long time classified as simply a different colour form of the beadlet, it is now recognised as a separate species. Unlike the beadlet, it does not appear to brood its young. [Up to 10 cm across]

Dahlia anemone - *Urticina felina*

The dahlia anemone has a sturdy appearance, with its short squat column covered in warts and its rather stout tentacles, but it is nevertheless a beautiful animal. A powerful predator, it can catch and devour active prey such as prawns and surprisingly large fish. Dahlias can occur in a variety of different colours and often have attractive banding on their tentacles as well as radiating patterns on the large oral disk. Gravel or shell fragments are usually adhered to the column so that when the anemone is fully retracted it is surprisingly inconspicuous. Dahlias are often seen singly but can also occur in dense patches at the bottom of shallow rocky gullies. Such aggregations are a marvellous sight to the passing diver, but must spell doom to many an unwary small fish. The surge conditions found in such gullies will of course make it more difficult for the anemones' prey to avoid the grasp of their tentacles. [Up to 20 cm across]

Snakelocks anemone - *Anemonia viridis*

The snakelocks anemone prefers the brightly lit, seaweed-rich areas of rocky reefs in shallow water (top photograph this page) to the darker world of cliffs and overhangs which many anemone species inhabit. It can also be found in pools on the shore and on kelp fronds or, in the case of small individuals, on eel-grass strands. The two hundred or so long wavy tentacles are very sticky and are often a rich green colour with beautiful purple tips; they are unusual in that they cannot be fully retracted. The tentacles may obscure the short and squat column which is tapered and irregular in cross-section. The sun-seeking habit of the snakelocks is related to the fact that the tissues of its tentacles contain large populations of special symbiotic algae. In this close association, the algae gain protection and a supply of carbon dioxide and nutrient salts; the host anemone benefits from organic compounds synthesised by the algae using sunlight as the energy source. The algae may also help to remove waste products

Snakelocks among seaweed on top of a reef

from its host's tissues. Snakelocks in deep or murky water are often a dull grey colour and this may be due to their algal populations becoming depleted in low light conditions. This species of anemone also has some sort of relationship with Leach's spider crab, *Inachus phalangium* (see page 58). The crabs seem content to reside around the base of smaller anemones but, when a larger anemone is their home (bottom photograph), they can be found living right in the

Small spider crab residing in snakelocks

centre. [With its long tentacles, the snakelocks can be up to 20 cm across]

Snakelocks anemone - *Anemonia viridis*

Plumose anemone - *Metridium senile*

There are few finer sights, in our waters or anywhere else, than a group of plumose anemones swaying in the current. Very familiar to divers, they are prominent animals and occur in large numbers covering expanses of sea bed or wreckage at many of the best diving locations. In its fully active state, the plumose anemone has a tall smooth column topped with a crown of very numerous fine, slender tentacles which give the characteristic feathery appearance. When withdrawn, it appears as a contracted little mound (see front right of photograph above). Individuals may be white, orange, green or brown in colour. Tentacles are usually, but not always, the same colour as the column (see above). Plumose anemones show a definite preference for areas of strong water flow, hence their frequent positioning on rock pinnacles or prominent pieces of wreckage. On wreckage, they seem to favour vertical surfaces such as on upright spars, rails and plates to horizontal positions. They may also be abundant in muddy areas, as long as there is some firm anchorage available. While normally most obvious down below the seaweed zone, plumose can be seen in shallow shady spots such as under overhangs and on jetty pilings; many superb portraits have been taken in only a few feet of water under Swanage Pier. With fine delicate tentacles, these anemones are unsuited to capturing the large animals, such as fish, that form the food of several other species. Instead, they specialise in smaller prey and their enzyme secretions can break down the shells of small planktonic crustaceans. As well as passing prey to the mouth in the usual anemone-like fashion of flexing whole tentacles, the plumose can use the hair-like flagellae and mucus strings on each tentacle to transfer food down to the oral disk. [Up to 30 cm tall]

Plumose anemone - *Metridium senile*

Trumpet anemone - *Aiptasia mutabilis*

Unlike most of the species described here, which can be found all around Britain, the trumpet anemone is only found in the South West and this represents the northernmost part of its distribution. It can be quite common, large numbers are found in Torbay for instance, but its kelp-like colouring means that it may stand out less than other anemones. The overall brown or khaki is broken up by distinctive white or pale blue lines on its disk which radiate out from the mouth. [Can apparently reach up to 15 cm across but usually 5 cm or less]

Actinothoe sphyrodeta

A common small anemone that can be found individually or in groups on rock faces. Most individuals are white all over but the disk is sometimes orange. The column and tentacles are always white. There are usually faint dark vertical stripes on the column, particularly visible when the anemone is contracted. This species can be confused with the all-white or white-orange forms of *Sagartia elegans* (see opposite) but *Actinothoe* has untidier-looking tentacles which are fewer in number, and no suckers on its column. [Up to 2 cm across]

Daisy anemone - *Cereus pedunculatus*

Can form carpets of many individuals or be found singly, often living on muddy sea beds where their bases are anchored to stones buried in the sediment. The anemone's long, slender column is hidden in the mud so its large disk and numerous short tentacles lie virtually flush with the mud's surface. Daisy anemones also live on rock where their columns are hidden in crevices. The disk may be a uniform brown or be attractively patterned in various colours, while the tentacles can be striped or mottled. There is often a bold splash of colour around the mouth. Young anemones develop within the parent and are released as fully formed miniatures. [Up to 10 cm across, more usually about 5 cm]

Sagartia elegans

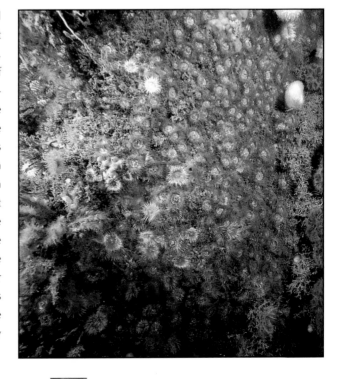

This anemone can be found in several different colour forms which, at first glance, look like separate species. The photograph shows individuals of the following forms: white tentacles-white disk, white tentacles-orange disk and pink tentacles-variable coloured disk. Further permutations are also possible. The column, which is usually dull orange, is covered with small wart-like suckers that are most obvious when the tentacles are withdrawn. Sticky white threads are sometimes released by the anemone if disturbed. Reproduction can either be sexual or by an asexual process where fragments of tissue separate from the base and form new anemones. [Up to 5 cm across]

Parasitic anemone - *Calliactis parasitica*

This species of anemone is usually found on second-hand mollusc shells inhabited by the large hermit crab, *Pagurus bernhardus* (page 60). The column of the parasitic anemone is typically a dirty cream colour with brown spots or stripes, while the tentacles are a yellowish grey. The anemone's name is misleading because it is in no way a parasite. Both crab and anemone benefit from the relationship and both can live independently; the anemone sometimes being found on stones or empty mollusc shells (top photograph, opposite page). Such a loose liaison is not true symbiosis either, and is normally referred to as commensalism. When living together, the crab will benefit from extra protection provided by the anemone's stinging tentacles against predators such as fish and cuttlefish. In return, the anemone receives extra scraps as the crab messily rips up its food, and gets free transport to different feeding locations.

As the crab moves around, the anemone will often bend over so its tentacles "sweep" the sea bed. Parasitic anemones can recognise hermit crab shells, probably by smell, and will actively transfer onto one if they are living on another substrate. First of all, they reach out and attach their oral disk to the shell with the aid of discharge capsules. They then detach their base from its current anchorage, and swing it across onto the hermit's shell. The crab plays no active part, but co-operates by keeping still. Occasionally, more than one parasitic anemone will be found on a single hermit crab. The bottom photograph on the opposite page shows a crab carrying three anemones, it could barely move under the weight. [Anemone up to 8 cm tall]

Parasitic anemone - *Calliactis parasitica*

Living alone

Three anemones on a single crab

Cloak anemone - *Adamsia carciniopados*

This is another species that lives on hermit crabs, but the association is much more intimate than that between the parasitic anemone and its host. The cloak anemone's host is the small hermit crab, *Pagurus prideauxi*. The anemone is never found living without a crab, and tends to stay with the same crab for life. Its base, which is usually brown or white with garish magenta spots, is wrapped right around the crab's mollusc shell home, hence the name "cloak". The anemone's white tentacles are positioned down between the crabs legs in an ideal position to pick up the scraps which inevitably result from the crab's feeding activities. By secreting a hard extension to the crab's residence, the anemone removes the crab's usual need to seek larger shells as it grows. This reduces stress for the crab and of course also prevents the anemone itself from being abandoned. When touched, the anemone releases sticky white threads from its "cloak" as a defence mechanism. This will often be seen to occur if a host hermit bumps into a rock or worm tube as it retreats hurriedly across the sea bed (top photograph, opposite page). On some anemones, the bright pink spots are obscured and it is only the emergence of these threads that give away their presence. The bottom photograph on the opposite page shows that a cloak anemone does not make its host invincible. A swimming crab is tucking into the remains of a small hermit crab while its cloak anemone looks to have been carefully peeled off and discarded. The anemone has discharged some threads in a last act of defiance. ["Cloak" up to 7 cm across]

Cloak anemone - *Adamsia carciniopados*

Defences activated

Not everyone is deterred. This swimming crab has removed and discarded the anemone, before tucking into the hermit crab.

Jewel anemone - *Corynactis viridis*

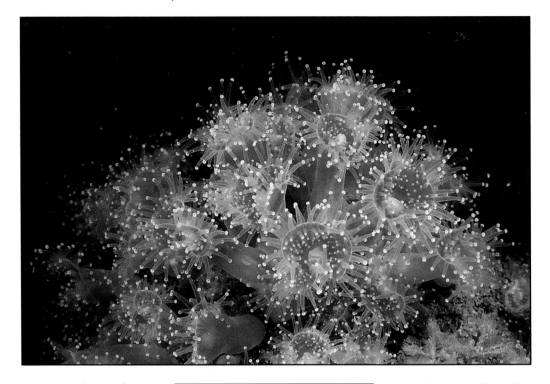

Small individually but impressive collectively, jewel anemones produce some of the most beautiful underwater scenery in the West Country. The anemones occur in an amazing variety of colours: pinks, purples, reds, yellows, greens, browns and more can all be seen on a single rock face. Their capacity for prolific asexual reproduction means that the different colours are not totally mixed but occur in distinct patches. When this

Jewel anemone patchwork

result is astounding. Like plumose anemones, jewels favour fast flowing water and the two species are often found together. Even if you ignore the wider picture and concentrate on an individual, the jewel anemone is an attractive animal. It has one hundred or so translucent tentacles, with distinctive white or brightly coloured rounded knobs on the tips; these knobs are laden with large numbers of discharge capsules of different types.

effect is combined with very clear water in locations such as the Eddystone Reef off Plymouth, Raglan Reef off the Lizard (bottom photograph this page) and the Scilly Isles, the The mouth is borne on a minute cone in the centre of the tentacles. Jewel anemones are actually more closely related to corals than to the other anemones. [Up to 2.5 cm. across]

Jewel anemone - *Corynactis viridis*

Burrowing anemone - *Cerianthus lloydii*

The burrowing anemone belongs to a different sub-group from the true anemones and, rather than attaching itself to a rock or similar firm surface, lives in a soft felt-like tube. Specially adapted discharge capsules are used to construct the tube. Although the tube can reach up to 40 cm in length, only its uppermost rim will protrude above the sand or mud in which the remainder lies buried. The anemone's tentacles are usually all that is visible. The innermost set are short and stiff, while the outer ones are longer and sometimes attractively banded. The tentacles themselves are not retractable but, when disturbed, the whole

Dislodged anemone and its tube

anemone shoots back into its tube. The smaller photograph, of a dead anemone in its dislodged tube, shows the relative proportions of anemone and tube. [Body/column up to 15 cm long, tentacle crown up to 10 cm across]

Devonshire cup-coral - *Caryophyllia smithii*

Abundant around much of the UK and not only Devon, this species is the only common stony coral in our waters. Stony corals are similar to sea anemones but produce hard chalky skeletons to support and protect their bodies. They are usually colonial animals, and their fused skeletons can then form large coral structures. Cup-corals, however, live alone and do not fuse together, although many can live within close proximity. Their hard skeleton consists almost entirely of calcium carbonate and is cup or goblet-shaped, with pronounced ridges radiating out from the centre and running over the rim. As the creature lays down more skeletal material at its base, it is pushed upward and stays in the top of the cup. With tentacles fully extended, cup corals resemble small anemones. There are many different colour forms and some have a very attractive zigzag pattern of dense colour around the central mouth, while others are all white. The tentacles end in small but obvious knobs. The underlying skeleton may be largely obscured (as above) or quite obvious (as in the cup corals in the foreground of the photograph of a cotton-spinner on page 96). Empty cup skeletons can sometimes be seen after the polyp has died. [Up to 4 cm across]

Dead men's fingers - *Alcyonium digitatum*

Like some species of anemone, the soft coral colonies known as dead men's fingers can cover large expanses of rocky cliffs or sea bed and so create their own brand of underwater scenery. Each "finger" is a colony of tiny animals that has formed a mutual skeleton of gelatinous material (hence soft coral) strengthened by embedded calcareous spicules. Until a colony reaches a height of about 5 cm it remains unbranched but, once larger than this, it tends to divide into several lobes. If arranged in a single plane as they often are, a group of lobes then appears like a hand. When active and feeding, the animals that make up the colonies extend their translucent tentacles and the lobes have a characteristically attractive "furry" appearance. Those in the lobe at the lower-right of the photograph have retracted their tentacles. In the autumn, most colonies stop feeding and withdraw their tentacles for several months, while they prepare to spawn. Entire rock faces can then be covered by what look like knobs of expanded polystyrene. When feeding is resumed, an outer skin is shed, along with any encrusting growths that settled while the tentacles were out of action. Dead men's fingers are most abundant down below the kelp zone and, as with many animals that rely on suspended food, they are more abundant in areas of moving water. In northern Britain, the orange form of dead men's fingers is very common but it is the white form that dominates heavily in the South West. [Up to 20 cm tall]

Red fingers - *Alcyonium glomeratum*

Close-up of tentacles

Not to be confused with the orange form of dead men's fingers, red fingers are a separate but closely related species of soft coral. The feeding tentacles are white, as opposed to the translucence of those belonging to dead men's fingers, and make a striking contrast against their red background. This allows extreme close-ups (main photograph) to show their full beauty. Further differences between the two species are that red finger colonies can be taller, and often

Colonies showing tentacles extended and withdrawn

appear slimmer, than those of their close relative and that they have a distinctly knobbly appearance when the tentacles are withdrawn (see bottom lobes in smaller photograph). Red fingers are far less common than dead men's fingers. [Up to 30 cm tall]

Sea fan - *Eunicella verrucosa*

Rocky slopes covered in sea fans might be more usually associated with exotic locations, but they are frequently encountered while diving by boat from such launch sites as Salcombe, Plymouth, Newquay, and Porthkerris on the Lizard. This species can also be found close to the shore but is far more abundant in deeper water locations. Like dead men's fingers, sea fans are colonies of tiny creatures. The sea fan is classified as a gorgonian or horny coral. A skeleton composed of a dark brown compound, gorgonin, reinforced with calcium carbonate, runs through the fan and is covered with fleshy tissue from which the tentacles of the numerous polyps emerge to feed. This tissue gives the fan its colour, orange, pink or white. Fans only branch in one plane which is usually at right angles to the prevailing current, thus giving each animal the maximum opportunity for feeding. With the majority of feeding polyps lifted well clear of the sea bed, reasonably silty conditions can be tolerated. Fans are fairly flexible but can easily be broken or dislodged from the rock by careless fin or arm movements. They are slow-growing and will die once knocked flat, so please take care! In some locations such as Lundy, a tiny species of sea slug can be found feeding on the fan's polyps, though these are thought to re-grow so the fan as a whole survives. The slugs' colouration matches the fan, and parts of their bodies mimic the protruding polyps, so they are extremely difficult to spot. [Fans up to 30 cm tall]

Oaten pipe hydroid - *Tubularia indivisa*

A species often found in large aggregations on rock faces exposed to strong currents. Numerous long and very thin straw-like stems rise up from a mat of tangled fibres to form dense bunches. These stems support polyps that have pink bodies bearing a crown of long white, rather droopy, tentacles. The reproductive parts appear like a bunch of grapes near the centre of the crown. This species produces a creeping larva rather than a free-swimming medusa and lives for about a year. A number of types of sea slug prey on this hydroid and can often be found amongst the stems, or crawling up them to feed on the polyps (page 78). The slugs are not deterred by the hydroid's stinging cells, some even incorporating them for their own defensive use. [Up to 15 cm tall]

Sea beard - *Nemertesia antennina*

This hydroid is found growing in distinct clumps. The main stems, pale orange or buff in colour, are unbranched but have numerous feathery side branches. Each stem in the clump is a colony of individual polyps, whose tentacles add to the furry appearance. The clumps provide shelter and food for small animals of all kinds and the white beads of sea slug eggs can often be seen

entwined round individual stems. When looking at this species, it is very easy to see why hydroids are also known as sea-firs. The brightly coloured creatures, visible on the rock face around the sea beard clumps, are jewel anemones (page 30). [Up to 25 cm tall]

Compass jellyfish - *Chrysaora hysoscella*

This species is easily identified by the attractive radial pattern of dark brown V-shaped markings on its "umbrella" or "bell". An additional dark circle in the centre of the pattern completes the appearance of an old-fashioned compass rose. Twenty-four slender (marginal) tentacles hang down from the edge of the umbrella while there are four much more noticeable (oral) arms in the centre. The marginal tentacles extend when the animal is hungry and, on capturing prey, contract in order to pass the food to the oral arms. When feeding is finished, the marginal tentacles remain contracted. Eight sense organs, each one situated between groups of three marginal tentacles around the

umbrella's fringe, enable the jellyfish to maintain its orientation in the water. The sting of this species can sometimes cause a painful reaction on exposed skin. [Umbrella up to 30 cm across]

Moon (or common) jellyfish - *Aurelia aurita*

Without long trailing tentacles, the moon jelly's most distinctive features are its reproductive organs which appear as four relatively opaque horse shoe-shaped tissues in its almost transparent umbrella. The umbrella itself is saucer-shaped and has numerous small tentacles around the edge, like a fringe. It has eight marginal sense organs like the compass jellyfish, and these are marked by slight indentations in the rim. The four arms near the central mouth are used in feeding, though planktonic food can also be captured in mucus anywhere on the

umbrella and be transported to the mouth by a system of grooves lined with tiny beating hair-like cilia. The short peripheral tentacles can also capture prey with their stinging cells, though these are not of sufficient power to bother humans. [Up to 25 cm across]

Rhizostoma octopus

This species is the largest jellyfish found in British waters. Not often found close to the shore, it is usually seen from boats or by divers decompressing on a shot-line, for whom its massive pulsating form makes an interesting diversion. There are no markings on the whitish umbrella except for its dark rim, and no peripheral tentacles. The eight central arms are fused for much of their length to form a dense bunched mass. This structure bears hundreds of tiny mouth openings, each surrounded by miniature tentacles bearing stinging cells. Creatures striking the tentacles and small enough to pass through a mouth opening will be ingested. The sting is harmless to humans and there are even reports of these jellyfish being eaten by eighteenth century fishermen. *Rhizostoma* is apparently very sensitive to the vibration from ships and will move downwards as one approaches. [Up to 80 cm across]

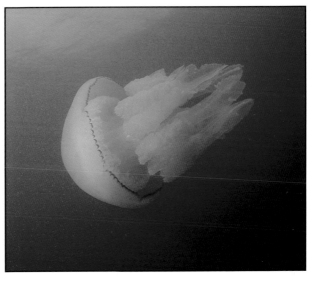

Lion's mane - *Cyanea capillata*

The lion's mane jellyfish is not usually very common in the South West but, when encountered, it can leave a painful impression! Its tentacles are up to three metres long when extended and are covered with powerful stinging cells. The umbrella usually has brown markings and is rather flat with its edge formed into large lobes. There are four large arms surrounding the mouth, but these are far shorter than the tentacles. The tentacles are arranged in eight bunches, with each bunch containing over a hundred tentacles, the oldest of which is often coloured dark red. It is very easy to swim into a tentacle and be stung before even knowing the jellyfish is there. Fragments of tentacles, left on buoy ropes for example, retain their stinging power. [Up to 50 cm across]

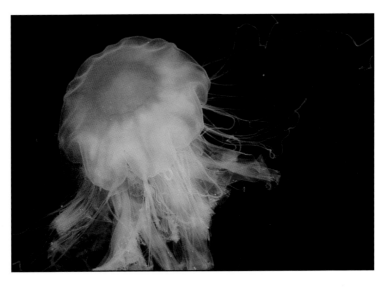

Chapter 4
WORMS

Few groups of animals would initially seem to be of less interest than the worms, but some of those that live in the sea are surprisingly attractive and definitely worthy of further scrutiny. The term "worm" is rather misleading because it tends to be applied to any creature that is long and wriggly. Different groups of animals, that vary enormously in terms of their biology and level of sophistication, fall into this category as a result. For ease of reference, different types of worm are all included in this chapter. Representatives of the flatworms and ribbon worms are dealt with on page 42, and the rest of the chapter belongs to the segmented worms. The characteristics of the different groups are described below.

Flatworms

Flatworms, forming the phylum Platyhelminthes, are primitive leaf-shaped animals. They are regarded as being more advanced than cnidarians (sea anemones, jellyfish) because of the way that they are organised. The cells that make up cnidarians are grouped to form tissues, but that is as far as organisation goes. The tissues of flatworms work together to form organs, that perform particular functions such as digestion. Flatworms are the lowliest animals to have this level of organisation, and may possibly represent the ancestral group from which all the other more advanced animals are descended. Flatworms are still classified as simple because they lack a body cavity, and this means that their internal layout has to remain fairly crude. Also, they only have a single opening to the digestive system, which has to serve as both mouth and anus. Flatworms like the candy stripe (page 42) are free-living, but many species are well known parasites of land animals; tapeworms and liver flukes are examples.

Ribbon worms

Ribbon worms make up the phylum Nemertea and, as their name implies, are thin and long. They are quite primitive but are slightly more advanced than flatworms. They have an anus as well as a mouth, which means that the intestine can utilise a more efficient one-way system where undigested and digested food are separated. This is a big advantage over the flatworms, whose food and excretion products have to enter and leave the body by the same route. Ribbon worms also have a circulatory system and possess more advanced muscles and nerve networks. A trunk-like extending structure, the proboscis, is used both in trapping prey and in defence.

Worm egg capsules attached to seaweed

Segmented worms

In contrast to flatworms and ribbon worms, segmented worms (belonging to the phylum Annelida) are quite complex animals on a par with most crustaceans and molluscs. They have a proper body cavity, which permits the development of sophisticated internal organs, while the nervous system is of sufficient complexity to support a variety of behaviour patterns. Virtually all the segmented worms found in the sea, and all those species described in this chapter, belong to the bristle worm sub-group. Typically, they have heads which bear intricate jaws, antennae and sense organs, while the remainder of the body consists of a series of less specialised segments which are fairly similar to one another. Many of these worms move freely from place to place but, because they burrow into soft sea beds or stay hidden amongst the organic

debris on rocky sea beds, they are rarely seen by snorkellers or divers. Some species, however, leave a very obvious clue to their existence every year in the early spring. They attach their green egg capsules to seaweed (see above), and these can be seen in huge numbers, forming an obvious part of the scenery. In general, however, the segmented worms that make themselves most obvious to the diver are those that have given up the free-living way of life, and live in a tube of their own construction. A good example is the aptly named sand-mason worm (page 44). Many of these species have heads and sense organs less well developed than those of their active relatives, but they have a crown of very specialised feathery tentacles. These can be surprisingly beautiful, and are extended into the water column where they are used both for respiration and for collecting suspended food.

Candy stripe flatworm - *Prostheceraeus vittatus*

Usually found on mud, the candy stripe flatworm is so thin and flexible it gives the impression of almost flowing across the sea bed. Colouration is distinctive, cream with very marked dark "pin-stripes", and its body is often thrown into folds at the edges. There are two tentacles at the head end of the body which makes the worm

look rather like a sea slug, but these are a totally different group of animals (see Chapter 6). Mobile flatworms such as *Prostheceraeus* are carnivorous and feed on slow-moving, sedentary or dead animals. Their smooth gliding motion is produced by thousands of tiny hair-like cilia on the under side of the body acting in unison. [Up to 3 cm long]

Bootlace worm - *Lineus longissimus*

Individuals of this very slender ribbon worm species can grow to over 30 metres in length, so it could be thought of as Britain's largest animal! More usually, they are around 5 metres long when extended, but the entire body is rarely visible and will contract rapidly if touched. Colouration is typically dark brown to almost black,

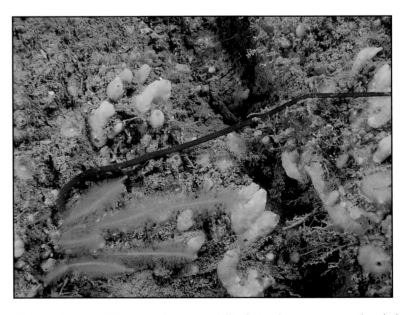

sometimes with a slight iridescent sheen. The head is only slightly wider than the rest of the body and has several eyes on each side, though these are difficult to discern against the dark pigment. [Up to 30m long]

Sea mouse - *Aphrodita aculeata*

A strange-looking animal that does not even look like a worm. The upper side of its broad and flattened body is covered with a felt-like fur while, round its edges, are some stout dark bristles and a fringe of silky iridescent hairs that can appear to glow gold, yellow and blue. The telltale worm-like segments are only visible on the body's underside. The sea mouse lives on bottoms of muddy sand and is usually buried with only its hind end exposed; it is thought to prey on other worms as well as eating carrion. The array of body hairs prevents mud particles being drawn in with the animal's breathing current. [Up to 20 cm long]

Lugworm - *Arenicola marina*

Worm cast

Whether on the beach or underwater, the cast of the lugworm is a very familiar sight. The worm itself is barely ever seen, as it has no need to leave its U-shaped burrow. Lugworms feed on the organic material in muddy sand and have to swallow enormous amounts of sediment in order to obtain adequate nutrition. The coiled casts represent processed material ejected by the worm while the small hollow in the sand nearby is where water, for respiration, and fresh sediment is drawn down. The long burrow is lined with mucus to prevent its collapse. [Worm up to 25 cm long; coiled casts up to 20 cm across]

Strawberry worm - *Eupolymnia nebulosa*

This photograph shows the worm's body, coloured in orange-pink with white spots, that gives rise to the name. It is, however, unusual to see anything more than the strawberry worm's long sticky tentacles (also shown in the photograph) which spread out over the sea bed to collect food particles. The tentacles shrink back rapidly if touched, but are not fully retractable. The body of the worm, and the slimy tube in which it lives, are usually hidden beneath stones and shell fragments on muddy sediment. Where many worms live close together, a real tangle of tentacles may cover the sea bed. [Body up to 15 cm long, tentacles 20 cm long or more]

Sand-mason - *Lanice conchilega*

Forest of sand-mason tubes

The sand-mason worm builds a gritty tube from grains of sand glued together with mucus. The top of the tube stands proud of the sea bed, and is crowned with a tuft of finger-like extensions, so the overall effect is that of a miniature tree. Large numbers usually live together, resembling a sparse forest as in the photograph. The worm itself is hardly ever seen, but it extends its sticky tentacles along the "tree's" branches to catch suspended food, and also out over the sea bed to pick up deposited food particles and any sand grains required for tube maintenance. The branches, which are orientated across the current, also serve to slow down water flowing past, so more suspended material collects around them. [Body up to 30 cm long, tube to 45 cm but only top 5 cm shows]

Fan worm - *Bispira volutacornis*

This species of fan worm is very common in the South West, and its attractive feathery tentacles are commonly seen emerging from the nooks, crannies and overhangs along the sides of rocky gullies and reefs. The worm lives in a tube, constructed from mucus and mud, that looks like a roll of thick grey paper. Tubes may be up to 20 cm long, but most of their length is usually hidden within the rock crevice. When extended, the all-white or brown-and-white banded tentacles form a double spiral. The tentacles have a number of functions, including the collection of suspended food and the extraction of oxygen from the seawater. They are also scattered with sense organs such as eyes. A shadow passing overhead, or sudden movement anywhere in the vicinity, will cause them to be rapidly withdrawn into the tube. The worms tend to live in small groups and while the retraction of individuals may often appear synchronised, those in some groups show marked variations in sensitivity and response time. A tube with tentacles withdrawn, and showing the typical pinched appearance, is at the top right of the photograph. [Tentacle crown up to 5 cm across]

Myxicola infundibulum

This worm's distinctive tentacles are webbed along almost all their length, so the crown resembles a small cone or funnel. It is just the flat, pointed and darkly coloured tips of the tentacles that are clearly separate. *Myxicola* lives in sandy and muddy areas and only the very end of its thick gelatinous tube, if any at all, protrudes from the sediment. The outer edges of the crown will be virtually flat on the sea bed when fully expanded. This species is very shy and may rapidly withdraw into its tube when approached. The photograph shows a group of three individuals, but they are usually seen singly. [Tentacle crown up to 5 cm across]

Peacock worm - *Sabella pavonina*

The peacock worm is a very striking animal, possessing a wonderful fan of tentacles that emerges from a prominent but slim tube. The tubes are most often found attached to stones in sand and mud, sometimes in large numbers, and they can also be found on rocks or shipwrecks. Water-borne particles captured by the worm's tentacles are sorted so that the largest are discarded, the smallest are eaten and intermediates are mixed with mucus and used for tube construction. The tentacles are usually colourful, often with red banding, and as with all tube worms they disappear quickly if approached at all clumsily. [Tubes up to 25 cm long, tentacle crown up to 15 cm across]

Coral worm - *Salmacina dysteri*

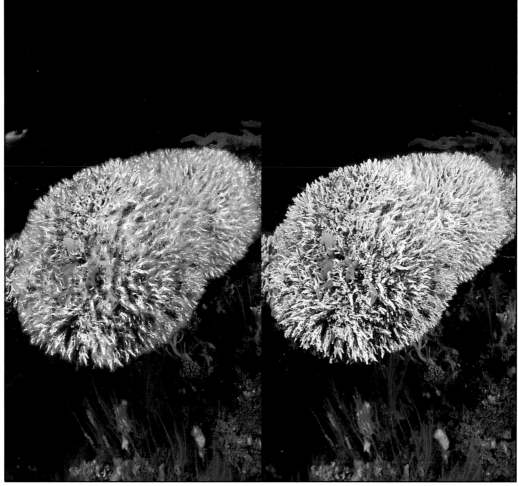

Tentacles out   Tentacles withdrawn

The coral worm is different from the other tube worms described in this chapter, in that its tube is hard and completely rigid. The tubes of many individuals are joined together to form a coral-like mass, hence the name. Colonies can be found attached to any hard surface; the photographs show one that has encrusted an undersea cable. The fine tentacles of each worm give the colony a "furry" appearance when extended for feeding (left-hand photograph), but this changes dramatically when they are withdrawn (right-hand photograph). The thin chalky tubes are manufactured almost entirely from calcium carbonate, the worms extracting calcium from seawater. Tube material is secreted by special glands, and is then moulded into shape by the collar near the worm's front end. Coral worms engage in some asexual reproduction (budding) and a new individual can be formed at the rear end of an existing one. The new worm will crawl part-way down the parent's tube and dissolve a small hole so that its own tentacles can emerge. If the parent tube is badly damaged by this activity it may become separated from the rest of the colony. [Individual worms tiny but colonies are often 15 cm across]

Chapter 5

CRUSTACEANS
Crabs, lobsters, prawns, shrimps & barnacles

Crustaceans can be thought of as the aquatic animals which wear suits of armour. This armour is jointed, and crustaceans belong to the larger grouping, Arthropoda, which means "jointed leg". The insects are also arthropods and, in many ways, the crustaceans are aquatic insects. All the familiar animals such as lobsters, crawfish, crabs, prawns and shrimps belong to the same sub-group of the crustaceans, the Decapoda, and have a similar body plan. They have ten legs (hence the name), the first pair of which are often claws. The head and thorax are fused and covered by a single section of armour, known as the carapace. The abdomen, or tail, is protected by further sections of armour and may be obvious as in the lobsters, prawns and shrimps or much reduced and tucked up as a flap underneath the rest of the body, as in the crabs. Barnacles, an unexpected inclusion in the crustacean category, are in a separate sub-group from these more familiar members. They are described in more detail on page 65. All the crustaceans described in this chapter have a larval phase that drifts as plankton in the open sea. On first hatching from the egg, these larvae look very different to adults, but they develop through various stages before assuming the adult form and taking up life on the sea bed.

A suit of armour, the benefits and drawbacks

The suit of armour worn by crustaceans has obvious benefits, providing good protection against predators, rigid anchorage points for powerful muscles and hard surfaces for crushing, cutting and grinding their prey. The major drawback is that it has to be shed periodically to allow growth. As a crustacean grows to fill its shell, it forms a soft leathery coat beneath the outer casing. At moulting time, the shell splits at a pre-determined point and the animal, clad in its soft coat, eases itself out. All the limbs, tiny mouth parts and even the eyes have to be removed from their casing and the complete suit of discarded armour can easily be mistaken for a dead animal. The top photograph, opposite, shows the discarded suit of a swimming crab; the opening at the back where the owner climbed out is visible. Having left the old suit, a soft crustacean swells itself up with water to create some growing room and the process of hardening up new armour then begins, taking several days in the case of large crabs and lobsters. The soft animal is obviously very vulnerable and has to stay as well hidden as possible. Once hard, it will have a particularly large appetite and seek food vigorously before eventually becoming relatively inactive and listless as it prepares for the next moult. Reproduction is affected by moulting, because the female of many species is only receptive after she has just shed her shell, so the moulting cycles of crustaceans can really be seen to dominate their lives. The bottom photograph on this page shows the sequence of armour suits worn and discarded by a shore crab kept in an aquarium. The amount of growth between successive moults is substantial.

Regenerating limbs

Although moulting inserts dangerous interludes into the life of a crustacean, it also provides the opportunity for regenerating limbs. A leg or claw that is

The suit of armour discarded by a moulting crab

Series of discarded suits showing the growth of a crab

damaged or seized by a predator can be jettisoned by the animal, which breaks it off deliberately at a particular point near to its base. A new limb can then start to form inside the shell and will emerge at the next moult. This is why crustaceans will often be seen with a very small leg or claw, though this will catch up with the other limbs over subsequent moults. The process can lead to a "right-handed" crab or lobster becoming "left-handed". If the large crushing claw is lost, the return to a fully equipped state can be hastened by converting the smaller cutting claw to a crusher and then growing a new cutting claw.

Velvet swimming crab - *Necora puber*

The body of this abundant and widespread crab is covered with short greyish-brown hairs that provide the velvet-like appearance. The most notable features however, are the bright red eyes and the blue lines on its legs and claws. As in all swimming crabs, the final section of the rear-most pair of legs is flattened to form a swimming paddle. Velvet swimming crabs tend to be

Crab breaking into top-shell

pugnacious and, when encountered, may rear up and spread their claws in defiance rather than shrinking away into a crevice. Very common on rocky and stony sea beds, they can also be found on sandy and muddy bottoms where they may dig themselves in. They are versatile feeders and, being fast-moving and agile, can catch prey such as fish and prawns. All sorts of bottom-living animals like worms and molluscs are also taken. The smaller photograph on this page shows a velvet swimmer tackling a top-shell. Lacking the strength to simply crush such a shell, the crab gradually chips away at its opening with one claw while the other claw is used for holding and

Velvet swimming crab - *Necora puber*

turning. Although often actively carnivorous, some populations of velvet swimmers have been found to eat large quantities of sea weed. Pairs of crabs in pre-mating embrace (top photograph, this page) are a common sight. As in most crab species, the female can only mate when soft just after shedding her armour, so a male will find a female and hang on to her until she is ready to moult. He carries her tucked beneath his body and continues to move around and behave much as normal, possibly helping her out of the old armour when the time arrives. The middle photograph shows a pair of velvet swimmers actually mating. This is easily distinguished from the pre-mating embrace because the female is upside down and therefore lying underside-to-underside with the male. The bottom photograph shows the ultimate result of such a union, a female is carrying a large mass of fertilised eggs (noticeably granular and usually orange) between her abdomen and underside. An egg-carrying female is said to be "in berry". [Carapace up to 10 cm across]

Pair before mating

Pair in the midst of mating

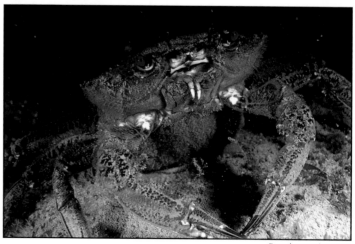

Female carrying eggs

Swimming crab - *Liocarcinus depurator*

This species, sometimes known as the common swimming crab or the harbour crab, is similar in shape to the velvet swimming crab but is more lightly built and pale pink or brown in colour. These swimming crabs are almost always found on sandy bottoms, sometimes buried with only eyes and antennae showing. If disturbed they have various options; making a rapid escape, assuming an aggressive posture with claws spread wide or simply moving a short distance and digging into the sediment. They are highly capable swimmers with a very distinctive style. The last pair of legs are used for paddles, as by all swimming crabs, but those of this species seem particularly well suited to the purpose, judged by both appearance and performance. The body is propelled rapidly sideways, just above the sea bed, with the other legs held stiffly out from

Pair before mating

the body for maximum streamlining. When swimming, the paddles are a blur of motion but, when stationary, the characteristic purple spots on the blades can be seen. Like the velvet swimmer, this species is often seen in pre-mating embrace (see smaller photograph). Note how the female is held in position by just one of the male's legs. [Carapace up to 7 cm across]

Shore crab - *Carcinus maenas*

Parasitised crab with heavy encrusting growth

The shore crab is classified as a swimming crab, and has a similar body shape to the two preceding species, but it is a much less accomplished swimmer. The last pair of legs is flattened but the final section is pointed rather than properly paddle-shaped. The shore crab's body is usually a shade of green or khaki, often with yellowish patterning, though deep brown or orange individuals are also seen. Common on the shore and in shallow water, this species is less familiar to divers than many crabs because it is most abundant in muddy estuaries and inlets. Shore crabs are extremely hardy creatures and will tolerate a wide range of conditions in terms of salinity and exposure to air, living in virtually fresh water or barely any water at all. Some populations suffer a high level of infestation from the parasitic barnacle, *Sacculina carcini*. This bizarre animal looks nothing like a normal barnacle and consists mainly of branching roots which penetrate the tissues of the unfortunate host crab. The parasite may give its presence

Healthy crab

away by the yellow reproductive mass beneath the crab's abdomen (distinguishable from the crab's egg mass because it is smooth rather than granular) but the clearest sign of a crab's infestation is that its carapace is covered with other encrusting animals. This is because the barnacle interferes with the crabs life to such an extent that moulting stops completely. The main photograph shows an infested crab and the smaller one a much healthier-looking individual, both from the Helford estuary in Cornwall. [Carapace up to 8 cm across]

Edible crab - *Cancer pagurus*

The edible crab has a thick, oval shell with a very distinctive "pie-crust" edging. The claws are large but the legs appear relatively small. The overall colour is a pink-brown but the claws have noticeable black tips. Compared to the swimming crabs, edible crabs are built very much for strength rather than speed. This is reflected in their prey, and molluscs that might require hours of patient manipulation from a velvet swimming crab can be quickly crushed by an edible crab's powerful claws. Conversely, they would find chasing small fish much more of a challenge than their nimbler relatives. Edible crabs are found in a variety of habitats at all depths. On rocky bottoms, they will live in crevices while, on soft sea beds, they dig themselves into the sediment. Here, they may also dig huge pits in their hunt for burrowing prey

Digging pit in search of food

such as clams and worms, and a muddy sea bed can become a mass of craters, each containing a busily excavating edible crab (see smaller photograph). As in all crabs, the abdomen of the female is broad and rounded while that of the male is narrower. [Carapace up to 25 cm across, but rarely more than 15 cm]

Masked crab - *Corystes cassivelaunus*

This crab is common on sandy sea beds, though it may be overlooked because it is usually only the tips of the antennae and claws that protrude from where it has dug into the sand. Masked crabs will often only be spotted when inadvertently disturbed and they may just move a short distance before digging in again. On occasion, they attempt to dig directly into the hiding place of another masked crab and the smaller photograph shows the altercation that resulted after one such intrusion. The crabs' short legs give them a relatively slow, lumbering gait. Males (as shown) have very long claws, up to double the length of the body, but those of the female are much shorter. Unlike that of the other crabs listed here, the carapace of the masked crab is longer than it is broad. Once tilted upright, the body is therefore the perfect shape to slip rapidly beneath the sand while the crab digs with its legs.

Territorial dispute

While buried, the antennae are held together to form a snorkel-like tube through which the crab can draw clean water. To the imaginative, the ridges on the carapace look like a human face, hence the name. [Carapace up to 5 cm long]

Square crab (or mud runner) - *Goneplax rhomboides*

The square crab has a most distinctive appearance and is unmistakable whether viewed from the front or the back. Its carapace is much broader than it is long and has very pointed corners, while the long eye-stalks and very long slender claws enhance the exotic image. Both photographs show male crabs. The female, which is seen less frequently, has

much smaller claws. This species is quite a rare sighting in most areas but it is abundant in certain locations, Brixham for instance. While many of the crab species described in this chapter can dig themselves into soft sediments, the square crab is different in that it makes a permanent burrow in the mud where it lives. The burrow is normally a shallow 'U' shape with two exits, but there may also be side tunnels. Crabs are often seen sitting at the entrance to their burrows, but they can also be found hiding in crevices beneath boulders or out and about on patches of mud between the boulders. Their detached claws are regularly seen lying on the sea bed in areas where they live, presumably lost in fights or during struggles with predators. [Carapace up to 5 cm across]

Spiny spider crab - *Maja squinado*

The carapace of this large crab is quite circular, shaped like a dome and covered in many short spines, with longer and more pointed spines around its edges. There are two large points between the eyes, looking almost like horns. It has long and slender legs, and the claws are not much bigger than the walking legs, except in large males. Spiny spider crabs can be found on most sea bed types, often resting in the open or wandering free rather than hiding in crevices. Despite these habits and their large size, some individuals can be very difficult to spot because of the camouflaging seaweed or sponge placed on their carapace and legs, which blends in perfectly with their surroundings. Spiny spider crabs can sometimes be seen grouped together in large heaps, or moving across the sea bed in substantial numbers, presumably on their way to or from such a function. The heaps are found in the summer, and may stay in the same place for a few months, often containing up to a hundred individuals. Huge mounds of up to a thousand crabs have even been reported. Crabs moult in the centre of the heaps and, while soft, are protected from predators by all the crabs outside them. The heaps also mean that newly moulted (and therefore receptive) females will have suitors readily available, so heaping seems to play an important part in the breeding of these crabs. Spiny spider crabs have a varied diet, feeding on seaweed and encrusting animals such as hydroids. They can also often be found eating carrion. [Carapace up to 20 cm across]

Leach's spider crab - *Inachus phalangium*

This small spider crab has a triangular carapace. The legs are very long and slender but the claws, which are usually held folded under the body, are fairly sturdy, particularly in the male. Carapace, claws and even legs are often covered with sponge and pieces of algae, which may make the crab virtually invisible. These crabs are very often seen hiding around the base of a snakelocks anemone or, if it is a large anemone, sitting within its tentacles (page 20). In some areas, virtually every snakelocks has its own resident crab. Both photographs show crabs with snakelocks; the two crabs in the smaller photograph appeared to be in dispute over the favoured space beneath the anemone's tentacles. The nature of the relationship between crab and anemone seems to be something of a mystery. *Inachus phalangium* is very difficult to distinguish from *Inachus dorsettensis*, the scorpion spider

Territorial dispute

crab, particularly as the distinguishing features on the carapace are usually obscured by camouflaging sponge. For the sharp-eyed, *I. dorsettensis* has a broad U-shaped tip to the promontory of its carapace between the eyes, while that of *I. phalangium* comes to a narrower point. [Carapace up to 3 cm across]

Long-legged spider crab - *Macropodia rostrata*

A small spider crab with an even more "spindly" appearance than the *Inachus* species described on the previous page. In addition to having a smaller body (especially in comparison to leg length) than *Inachus*, it lacks protrusions to the carapace behind the eyes, so the eye stalks are more prominent. It is very common but the emaciated features, coupled with the crab's habit of attaching camouflaging seaweed or sponge to its carapace and legs, can easily result in it being overlooked. It is most likely to be spotted while wandering across a sandy or muddy sea bed, away from any seaweed cover. A very similar species, the slender spider crab *Macropodia tenuirostris*, has a longer promontory at the very front of its carapace, though this is usually obscured by the seaweed camouflage. [Carapace up to 1.5 cm across]

Spiny squat lobster - *Galathea strigosa*

A striking creature with a brilliant red carapace, decorated by blue patches and stripes, and long red-tipped claws covered with a "fur" of brown spines. The body is long, but flattened, so it looks like a cross between a crab and a lobster. The tail is folded under the body and can be used as a paddle for rapid backward escape. These animals are rarely seen in their full glory, because they usually hide in narrow crevices, often clinging upside down to the rock ceiling and shrinking further out of view when approached. They are most likely to be seen out and about at night. A similar but smaller relative, *Galathea squamifera*, is greenish-brown. [G. *strigosa* - body up to 10 cm long. G. *squamifera* - body up to 6 cm long (including tail in both cases)]

Hermit crab - *Pagurus bernhardus*

Only the front part of a hermit crab is protected by the usual crustacean armour. The soft back end is protected by a disused mollusc shell which is carried around by the crab. When threatened, the whole body can be withdrawn into the shell with the larger right-hand claw forming a barrier across the entrance. The rear end of the hermit is coiled so that it fits neatly into the shell and is equipped with small hooks for clinging to it, while the last two pairs of walking legs are used as struts to support the shell's weight. As the crab grows, a larger shell is sought out and the hermit will only change home after a prolonged and thorough inspection of the new shell. The top photograph on the opposite page shows a crab that seemed to be engaged in such an inspection, an ambitious gesture since the original mollusc owner was still in residence. Young hermits live in shells from smaller molluscs like winkles, while adults inhabit the larger whelk shells.

Hermit crabs are versatile feeders and can prey on other animals, scavenge on bottom deposits or filter food from the surrounding water. Male hermits can be seen dragging females around for a few hours prior to mating (bottom photograph, opposite page) though the crabs found doing this are often surprisingly small. *Pagurus bernhardus* is common on both rock and sandy sea beds. A smaller relative, *Pagurus prideauxi*, is a darker red-brown in colour and usually lives on muddy bottoms. Both species can be associated with certain types of sea anemone (see pages 26-29). Other animals, such as worms, may live on the shell or even inside it with the crab in order to gain protection and/or extra food. [*P. bernhardus* - carapace up to 4 cm long, but mollusc shell home makes crab appear much larger. *P. prideauxi* - carapace up to 1.5 cm long, though many small crabs will simply be young individuals of the larger species]

Hermit crab - *Pagurus bernhardus*

Examining a potential home

Pair before mating

Common lobster - *Homarus gammarus*

A "left-handed" lobster at home

A "right-handed" lobster out and about

Common lobster - *Homarus gammarus*

A magnificent but all too rare sighting, the lobster's appearance is unmistakable: dark blue armour with pale yellow markings and long bright red antennae. The powerful claws are quite different in shape; one (usually the right-hand one) is heavier and is used for crushing, while the other is a sharper cutting tool. Lobsters are normally found hiding within rocky holes or inside wrecks during the day but, when watched for a while, may move cautiously forward to investigate the intruder. They will usually only emerge from their lair at night, but can occasionally be seen roaming the sea bed during the day (see bottom photograph, previous page). Such encounters normally happen in deep water but lobsters may also be found in very shallow water if there is sufficient shelter. They feed on a variety of bottom-living animals, alive or dead, and are also well known cannibals; it is difficult to keep more than one lobster in an aquarium because the first one to moult will usually be rapidly consumed by its companion. They generally move by walking, but can also swim rapidly backwards in short bursts by using the powerful tail as a paddle. Mating is thought to occur in the late summer, but females can store the sperm packet over the winter so the eggs are not fertilised and laid until the following summer. They may then take a further year to hatch into the free-swimming larvae. After a few moults, these transform into miniature lobsters and settle on the sea bed. Large lobsters moult only very occasionally, if at all, and can become covered with barnacles and other encrusting organisms. They may live for up to 50 years. [Body up to 75 cm long but rarely more than 30 cm]

Crawfish (or spiny lobster) - *Palinurus elephas*

The crawfish is a large animal with strong, spiky body armour but no claws. Colouration is orange brown with yellow markings. The antennae are longer than the body and heavily built, with large spines at their bases so that they can be used as defensive weapons. Crawfish live in rocky areas and may often be found in holes, but they are also more likely to be seen wandering free over the sea bed during the day than the common lobster. They are rare in water shallower than 20 metres however. Numbers of these animals have

been greatly reduced by intensive fishing, chiefly carried out by divers. [Body up to 50 cm long but rarely more than 35 cm]

Common prawn - *Palaemon serratus*

These animals are a very common sight in the nooks and crannies of wrecks and rocky reefs, and are often found in groups. The almost transparent body has numerous delicate brown lines and there may also be obvious yellow bands and blue markings on the legs. The front two pairs of legs bear nippers, which are used to pick up small pieces of food as the prawn walks across the sea bed. Prawns can also swim, either backwards in rapid bursts using the tail fan, or forwards using the small flaps beneath the abdomen for propulsion. Surprisingly, groups of prawns often seem to occupy the same crevice as predators such as velvet swimming crabs, lobsters and congers. [Up to 10 cm long]

Brown shrimp - *Crangon crangon*

The brown or common shrimp is abundant in sandy areas but can be very difficult to spot because of its mottled sandy colouration and tendency to remain buried with only the eyes exposed. The shrimp's head and body are more flattened than those of the prawn and they lie almost flush with the sea bed, rather than being lifted up by the legs. Only the front pair of legs bear claws but these are more substantial than the prawn's. If a shrimp is seen walking across the sand it may rapidly dig itself in, using an odd shuffling motion to get started, followed by sweeping movements of its long antennae to brush sand over its back. [Up to 9 cm long]

Barnacle - *Balanus perforatus*

Barnacles belong to a totally different sub-group of crustaceans from all the other animals described in this chapter. On first glance, one would not even think of them as crustaceans at all. With their sedentary life-style and limpet-like shape, barnacles look rather like molluscs, which was how they were classified until 1830. As with other examples in the animal kingdom, it was an examination of their larvae (which look like those of other crustaceans) that revealed their true identity. A barnacle has been described as being "like a shrimp which glues its head to a rock, lives in a house and kicks food into its mouth". This is entirely accurate, as glands on the young barnacle's head produce a special cement for permanent attachment, the usual crustacean armour is modified to form flat plates that make up the "house", and the limbs form a sieve for catching plankton. When observed underwater the rhythmic sweeping of the feeding "sieve", looking rather like a grasping hand, can be seen (see photograph). The limb is rapidly withdrawn if sudden movement is detected and small fish can sometimes be seen trying to nip it off before this happens. Barnacles occur in large populations on the shore and in shallow water. They are hermaphrodites (simultaneously male and female) and mating usually occurs between neighbours. The resulting embryos develop in the body of the parent until they become free-swimming larvae, and these then develop further until they are ready to take on adult life. It is at this point that they glue themselves head-first to a rock and quickly assume the familiar adult form. There are several very similar common species of barnacles, including other *Balanus* species, which have an identical basic lifestyle. *Balanus perforatus* has simply been included as an example of its kind. [Up to 3 cm across]

Chapter 6
MOLLUSCS
Sea snails, sea slugs, bivalves & cuttlefish

The typical mollusc has a hard chalky external shell, formed in either one part (limpets, whelks) or two (mussels, scallops). Some molluscs however, have no shell at all (nudibranch sea slugs) or one that is hidden from view (cuttlefish) and these less typical molluscs are some of the most fascinating marine animals on view. Where present, the external shell is like a cover rather than the all-encompassing body armour of crustaceans. This means it can be gradually enlarged as the animal grows and does not have to be shed periodically, the same shell being kept for life. The phylum name, Mollusca, is derived from the Latin word for soft, in reference to the soft body typically enclosed in the hard shell.

Main mollusc features

The soft body of a typical mollusc is composed of three main parts: a muscular foot, a visceral mass which contains digestive and reproductive organs and, thirdly, a region of mantle tissue that secretes the shell. The very strong muscular foot forms the base of the animal and represents most of its contact with the outside world. The head, where sensory organs such as eyes and tentacles are located, is formed from the front end of the foot. The mollusc shell is made up of a protein matrix reinforced by numerous calcium carbonate (chalk) crystals to produce a strong composite material like fibreglass.

Unusual feeding machinery

An intricate feeding mechanism, the radula, is found in most molluscs (apart from the bivalves) but nowhere else in the animal kingdom. It is a ribbon of horny tissue, bearing teeth, which is drawn backwards and forwards across food like a file. It also acts like a conveyor belt in transporting the rasped off food to the digestive tract. The form of the radula varies between molluscs that browse vegetation and those that eat flesh. The hard working machinery is continually replaced, with new teeth produced at one end of the radula while worn teeth are broken off at the other end.

Sea snails

These are the archetypal molluscs with a single hard shell, like limpets, whelks, top-shells and winkles. Many have a shell in the shape of a coil. They follow the basic mollusc body plan quite closely.

Sea slugs

Few animals arouse such interest relative to their size as the colourful sea slugs. Although some sea slugs have a reduced shell, most of the species encountered are of the nudibranch order which lack a shell entirely. The term nudibranch actually means "naked gill" because the gills have no shell or mantle cavity to protect them.

Without a hard shell into which they can retreat, nudibranchs have to rely on other forms of defence. Special skin glands produce toxins to repel predators and some species have an even more impressive system whereby they feed on creatures with stinging cells (sea anemones, hydroids) and utilise the second-hand discharge capsules for their own defence (see page 78). All sea slugs are hermaphrodites, having both male and female sex organs. When two come together to mate, there is usually double copulation with both individuals donating and receiving sperm. Sea slug egg masses are a very common sight attached to rocks, stones or hydroids. They are usually white and their appearance can vary from coiled flat ribbons to miniature strings of pearls. Only a fraction of the large number of nudibranch species that can be seen are described in this chapter. For a full listing, one of the more specialist texts needs to be consulted.

Bivalves

These are molluscs with two halves to their shells such as mussels and scallops. Bivalves have no head and are the only molluscs to do without a radula. The name bivalve means "two shells" but the shell is actually a single structure. The narrow strip of shell joining the two halves has much less calcified reinforcement than the rest, so it can act as a flexible hinge. Though they appear static and rather unsophisticated, bivalve molluscs are highly specialised for their chosen way of life, namely filter feeding. The gills are enormous, far larger than would be needed just for respiration, because they are also used for collecting suspended food from the water. Numerous banks of cilia (tiny hairs) on the gills beat in unison to create a powerful water current through the body cavity while other cilia help to trap food particles and move

them towards the gut. It is this filtering ability that can make bivalves dangerous purveyors of food poisoning when harvested from polluted areas. In addition to relatively obvious bivalves, such as mussels and scallops, there are numerous other types that burrow deep into soft sediment. From the surface of the mud or sand, the only sign of their presence is the two holes formed by the water intake and outflow tubes, which are rapidly withdrawn if any disturbance is detected.

Cuttlefish

Cuttlefish, along with octopus and squid, belong to a specialised group of molluscs, the cephalopods. The muscular foot of typical molluscs has become the group of tentacles attached to the head (cephalopod means "head-foot") and the mantle tissue has formed a jet propulsion organ, but it is still quite difficult to visualise how the basic mollusc body plan has been adapted to produce such sophisticated animals. Rather than having separate nerve centres scattered round the body like other molluscs, these animals have them fused and enlarged to form a sophisticated brain which is enormous by the standards of invertebrates. [Invertebrates are animals without proper backbones - all the animals in this book, except for the fish, are invertebrates]. The cephalopod brain is responsible for sophisticated behaviour and these animals display the ability to learn and remember for several weeks. Octopus and squid are rarely seen in West Country waters, but the frequently encountered and fascinating cuttlefish provide ample compensation.

Blue-rayed limpet - *Helcion pellucidum*

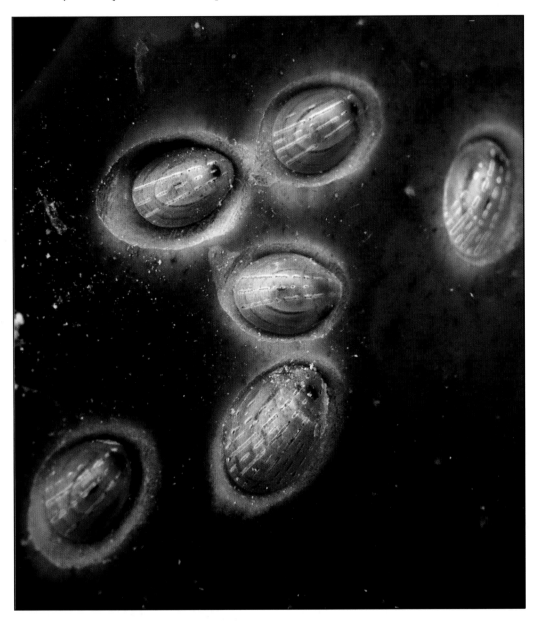

This beautiful little animal is only found on kelp plants, so it is often overlooked by divers and snorkellers to whom the swaying forests of kelp appear relatively unappealing. The delicate, slightly translucent shell is usually kelp coloured and would be unremarkable if it was not marked by broken lines of a wonderful kingfisher blue. The limpets are often found in small groups and each one excavates its own little pit into the kelp frond or stalk as it feeds. Some of these limpets appear to move down the kelp as autumn approaches, so they avoid being cast adrift when the frond is lost or damaged in winter storms. A different variety of the same species has a rougher shell with less prominent blue markings, and lives down in the holdfast of the kelp. [Shell up to 2 cm across]

Limpets - (various *Patella* species)

Many molluscs, such as winkles, that are largely restricted to the sea shore are omitted from this book; but common shore limpets are worth a mention because of an intriguing habit that reveals itself to anyone who glances beneath the sea's surface. Limpets create a "home base" on the surface of a rock by grinding their shell (or the rock if it is soft) to make a perfect fit. This helps to prevent the animal drying

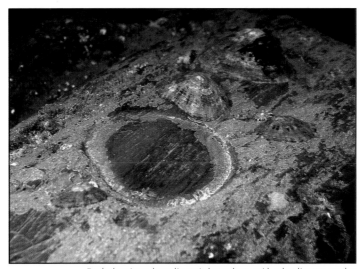

Rock showing a large limpet's home base, with other limpets nearby

up when the tide is out. When the tide is in, limpets leave their "home base" (visible as a scar on the rock - see photograph) and go off to graze on the rock nearby. They have to return home before the tide goes out again, and they navigate by following the trail of mucus which they left on the way out. Some sort of memory has also been suggested.

Painted top-shell - *Calliostoma zizyphinum*

The shell of this mollusc is in the shape of a sharply-pointed, straight-sided cone. Shell colouration is usually an attractive yellowish pink with streaks and blotches of crimson or brown. All white individuals may also be found. The animal apparently keeps its shell clean by rubbing it with its extendable foot on a regular basis. Like all top-shells, *Calliostoma* is a grazer and feeds on algae and other tiny organisms that live on the rock surfaces over

which it crawls. In the summer, it can sometimes be found laying its long gelatinous egg ribbon which is attached to stones or rock. The photograph shows two top-shells on the orange sponge, *Esperiopsis fucorum* (page 14). [Shell up to 3 cm across]

Slipper limpet - *Crepidula fornicata*

Now widespread around the south of Britain, this species was accidentally introduced from America back in the 19th century. It arrived in a shipment of oysters which were then re-laid for fattening on British oyster beds. The shell is a flattish oval shape and has a large shelf across its opening, visible when turned over (see top photograph), which gives it the appearance of a slipper. Its most remarkable feature is the way in which it forms stacks of up to twelve individuals (the bottom photograph shows a stack of four). Larger stacks tend to be curved like an arch, hence the specific name of *fornicata*, Latin for arch. The large limpets at the bottom of a chain are female, the small ones at the top are

Shell opening with shelf, producing the "slipper" shape

Stack of four limpets

male and the ones in between are, as one might suspect, in between. The animals change from male to female as they grow older. A young slipper limpet settling on its own develops into a female relatively rapidly, while one settling at the end of a chain will spend some time as a functional male. It appears that females secrete a sort of hormone into the water which maintains the masculinity of nearby males. The adult animals are immobile but males use their long penis to fertilise a female within the chain. Dense masses of slipper limpets are found in various locations, near Weymouth for example, and seem to take over the sea floor. They are filter feeders and can be a serious pest to oyster beds through crowding and competition for planktonic food. [Shell up to 5 cm long]

European cowrie - *Trivia monacha*

The cowrie's shell is shiny and appears highly polished but, in an active animal, it is almost completely obscured by folds of soft mantle tissue which extend from the entrance in the base of the shell. These folds have a rather striking pattern, a little like that of fake leopard-skin. The pale shell is traversed by delicate ribs and there are three dark blotches along its top (the blotches are absent on the shell of *Trivia arctica*, a close relative). These cowries eat colonial sea squirts, also laying their eggs in holes bitten out of the colonies. The photograph shows a cowrie crawling across sand, but they are more commonly found on rocks and stones. [Shell up to 1.5 cm long]

Netted dogwhelk - *Hinia reticulata*

Dogwhelks feeding on a crab carcass

This animal is a very common sight on sand, particularly where there are rocks nearby. It has a conical shell, distinctively marked with a neat rectangular pattern (hence the name) formed by the interaction of flat ribs and spiral ridges. A long siphon is usually held aloft and draws water down to the animal for breathing, even when the shell is completely buried in the sand. The incoming water is also tested for evidence of carrion and these animals can detect food at a considerable distance. They are often found gathered in large numbers on a fish or crab carcass (see photograph) and a search of the sand nearby usually reveals several latecomers hurrying to the feast. [Shell up to 3 cm long]

Sea hare - *Aplysia punctata*

The sea hare (and *Pleurobranchus* opposite) are both sea slugs, but have a much reduced shell that is hidden by the soft tissues. The other slugs described in this chapter are nudibranchs and have no shell at all. The sea hare has large flap-like lobes of tissue on its back and two pairs of tentacles on the head. The upper pair are broad, like hare's ears, hence the name. Colouration may be brown, olive-green or dark red, often with blackish spots and veining. Sea hares are herbivores and the type of seaweed they eat may affect their colour. Individuals eating the appropriately named food of sea lettuce are thought to be green, while those eating red seaweeds (usually younger sea hares) can be almost maroon. Many sea slugs secrete a noxious chemical as a defensive mechanism and the sea hare uses a two-part mixture of foul-tasting whitish slime and vivid purple fluid, each produced by separate glands. The sea hare is a

Mating chain and pink egg string

hermaphrodite like all sea slugs, and has a particularly interesting sex life. Although incapable of fertilising itself, any individual can act as either a male or female to another. Several sea hares will sometimes form a mating chain where each behaves as a male to the one below it and as a female to the one above. The smaller photograph shows such a chain and also a pink strand of sea hare egg string. [Up to 20 cm long but usually much smaller]

Pleurobranchus membranaceus

Laying egg ribbon

This large sea slug has a pale brown body, usually with patches of darker brown, which is covered in soft tubercles that give it a "warty" appearance. Its mantle tissue forms a skirt around the body. The slug shown in the main photograph, found in the Helford estuary, was in the midst of producing its coiled egg ribbon which may contain more than one million eggs. This species feeds on sea squirts by drilling through their tough outer tunic and sucking out the soft insides. Like the sea hare, it has an internal shell hidden by the soft tissues. With no protection offered by the shell, potential predators are deterred by sulphuric acid which is produced by the skin and released if it is broken. *Pleurobranchus* can swim well, always in an upside-down position, using undulating

Swimming

movements of its foot (smaller photograph). Very occasionally, huge populations have been witnessed undertaking swimming migrations. The purpose of these is a mystery but aggregation for mating seems to be the most likely reason. [Up to 12 cm long]

Lomanotus genei

Mating pair

This wonderfully flamboyant sea slug is a nudibranch, and lacks a shell entirely. Its colour can vary from white through pink and orange to red, but it is characterised by a distinctive frill of protuberances with yellow or orange tips along the body. The main photograph shows a mating pair. As is typical with nudibranchs, the pair manage to both act as male and female during mating, thus fertilising each other simultaneously. The smaller photograph shows a single animal for ease of recognition. *Lomanotus* feeds on hydroids and winds its egg string around them at spawning time. It can swim clumsily if disturbed. [Up to 9 cm long]

Okenia elegans

Laying eggs

The body of this beautiful nudibranch sea slug is basically white, but may have such dense red freckles that it appears pink. There is a brilliant yellow border around the base of the body and the gills and various body protuberances are also splashed with yellow. The pair of tentacles, known as rhinophores, on the upper side of the head are highly convoluted and patterned in red and white with pale tips. The photographs show a pink slug laying its eggs and a virtually white individual crawling across the sea bed. *Okenia* feeds on sea squirts by burrowing into them, so it is often only the tips of the feathery gills that can be seen. It is usually classified as a rare species

but is quite a common sight in Plymouth Sound and around Torbay. [Up to 8 cm long]

Polycera faeroensis

The translucent white body of this common nudibranch tends to appear slightly swollen. Various parts of it are splashed with bright yellow, such as the distinctive tapering extensions around the front of the head (of which there are eight or more). There is also yellow on the tips of the pair of tentacles on top of the head, on the gills towards the rear, and on the protuberances next to them. A closely related species, *Polycera quadrilineata*, is similar in appearance but has fewer tapering extensions at the very front of the head (usually four) and splashes of yellow or orange forming several lines down the body itself. [Up to 5 cm long]

Janolus cristatus

This species, while not as colourful as some of its relatives, is still particularly striking. The pale translucent body is covered by numerous finger-like projections that appear rather bloated. A thin dark thread of digestive gland runs down the centre of each projection, sometimes forming tributaries near its end. There are splashes of an iridescent bluish-white pigment on the tips of the projections, and also in patches on the rest of the body. It is a fairly widespread animal, but is thought to be restricted to calm water because of its fragility. Its egg string looks like a wavy string

of tiny white beads; each bead contains around 250 individual eggs. [Up to 8 cm long]

Sea lemon - *Archidoris pseudoargus*

The sea lemon is a large and very common nudibranch of West Country waters. The upper side of its body is covered in small wart-like bumps and usually bears blotchy markings which can be any combination of yellow, pink, white, brown or green. A ring of feathery gills sticks up from near the animal's rear but is retracted quickly on the sensing of any disturbance. Sea lemons feed exclusively on encrusting sponges, chiefly the breadcrumb sponge (page 13), and their seemingly garish colouration can actually make them extremely difficult to spot when they are crawling across a mass of sponge. The smaller photograph shows a sea lemon's egg ribbon, which is laid in a coil with its bottom edge attached to the substrate, so a characteristic rosette is formed. Another

Slug laying egg ribbon and completed rosette

ribbon is being laid in the background. The sea lemon's entire life cycle is completed within a year. Adults mate and spawn in the spring before dying, and the new juveniles appear in the late summer and grow through the autumn and winter. [Up to 12 cm long]

Coryphella browni

The body of this nudibranch is a translucent white but the numerous long and pointed projections, or cerata, on its back contain brightly coloured (usually crimson) tributaries of the digestive gland. There is also a broad and very obvious white band near the tip of each projection. *Coryphella browni* feeds on hydroids such as the oaten pipe (page 37) and can often be found munching away at their polyps while perched on the straw-like stems (see photograph). Not only is it undeterred by their stinging abilities, it is one of the nudibranchs that ingests the stinging cells of such animals and puts them to its own use. The slug passes the intact cells through its digestive system and out to the cerata tips, where they are used for defence against predators. A hungry fish that attacks the slug is almost bound to nip one of the cerata, causing a stinging cell to discharge and the attack to be abandoned. Egg masses of this species, which look like wavy white threads, are often laid amongst the hydroid stems. Several other nudibranch species, some of which belong to the same *Coryphella* genus, have a very similar appearance. [Up to 5 cm long]

Common mussel - *Mytilus edulis*

The curved, two-halved mussel shell in blue, black and brown is instantly recognisable. Mussels normally live in large aggregations on the shore or in shallow water, attaching themselves to the rocks and each other with sticky threads known as byssus. A highly extendable foot reaches out from the shell to plant these threads, like setting the guy ropes of a tent.

Water is pumped into the mussel via the frilly-edged opening, and leaves by the smooth-edged outflow tube, both visible when the shells are gaping. Despite their tough shells, mussels may be pulled open by starfish, drilled into by dogwhelks or attacked from the inside by tiny pea crabs. [Shell up to 10 cm long but usually much smaller]

Great (or king) scallop - *Pecten maximus*

Unlike the mussel, the two shell halves differ greatly in shape. The lower is curved like a bowl, while the upper is flat, like a lid. Both halves bear distinctive radiating ribs. Scallops use a rocking motion to make a hollow for themselves in sand or gravel, where they sit with shells gaping as they feed. The attractive patterning on the soft tissue "curtain" can then be seen, along with the numerous small tentacles and tiny eyes with their metallic

blue sheen. Scallops swim rather comically by rapidly flapping their shells, the soft tissues guiding the resulting water jets to give some control over direction. Tiring quickly, the swimming range is small, though quite enough to escape a predatory starfish. [Shell up to 15 cm across]

Common cuttlefish - *Sepia officinalis*

The cuttlefish is probably the most fascinating animal encountered in our waters, and the next five pages are intended to introduce its intriguing nature. Very small individuals of this species could be confused with the little cuttle, *Sepiola*, (see page 85) but otherwise it is unmistakable. The broad and slightly flattened body, up to 30 cm long, is fringed by a fin on each side which runs from just behind the head right back to the rear. The mouth is surrounded by eight arms, two of which are sometimes raised above the head when approached. There are also two much longer, extendible tentacles hence the classification of decapod (ten feet). If startled, a cuttlefish may use its full escape mechanism, where the body assumes a shape for maximum streamlining and a powerful burst of jet propulsion thrusts it rapidly backwards. At the same time, it can release a cloud of black ink which will hang in the water and momentarily distract a pursuer while the cuttlefish escapes. If still pursued, larger clouds of ink are poured out. Once used by artists, the ink was called sepia, as in the animal's Latin name. If not startled when first encountered, the cuttlefish may well move slowly away, using a little gentle jet propulsion aided and stabilised by the rippling motion of its fringing fins. It is then that their most impressive skill, the total control of colour and patterning, can be appreciated. They may be less famous for it, but cuttlefish are much more skilful colour-change artists than even chameleons. If a cuttlefish swims off over a varying sea bed, its shade can change instantly to match its surroundings, going dark over kelp-covered rocks and almost white over sand. The animal seems to

Common cuttlefish - *Sepia officinalis*

calculate all the angles, apparently matching the sea bed against which the observer is seeing it, rather than that directly below it. If it comes to rest on the bottom, it will blend in perfectly. The top photograph on this page shows a cuttlefish as it first comes to sit on a gravel sea bed; a few seconds later (middle photograph) it has matched the gravel perfectly. To further improve camouflage, projections on the skin's surface will change its texture to replicate that of the surroundings. Cuttlefish will also flick sand or gravel up over themselves and gradually sink into the sea bed, leaving only the tops of their heads and backs exposed. When in such a position, only the most sharp-eyed diver will spot them. In addition to simply matching their surroundings, cuttlefish use all sorts of patterns in an attempt to break up their outline and generally confuse potential predators. From birth, young cuttlefish can display at least thirteen types of body pattern, made up from over thirty different components. Whatever the exact purpose of them all, and even the scientists who have logged them all remain unsure of this, watching a cuttlefish

This cuttlefish has just settled on a gravel sea bed

A few seconds later, it has matched its background

Another individual, showing the white square pattern

Common cuttlefish - *Sepia officinalis*

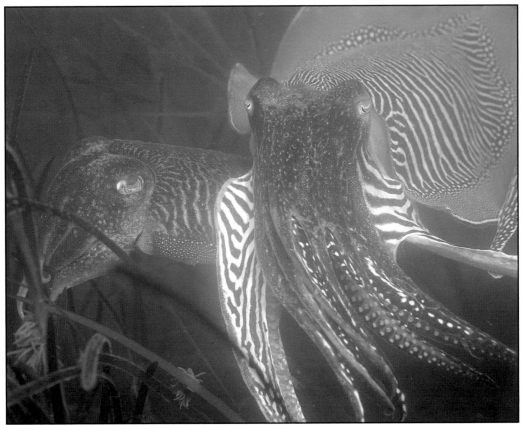

A courting couple, the male with dramatic stripes

flash through part of its repertoire is an awe-inspiring sight. One of the most common patterns is known as the "white square" (bottom photograph, previous page) which is accompanied by a white stripe on the head and a small white triangle at the rear. The secret of rapid pattern change is explained by the presence of special cells, known as chromatophores, within cuttlefish skin. These are effectively little flexible bags of pigment which, when expanded by muscular action, make the area of skin appear dark. When the bags are allowed to contract under the power of their own elasticity, the skin appears pale. In addition to avoiding predators, pattern control is also used in courtship. Male cuttlefish display brilliant zebra stripes at courting time in order to impress females and warn off competitors (see above). Mating is achieved by the male passing the female a packet of sperm, using one of his arms specially adapted for the purpose. After mating, a male will often defend the female while she lays her eggs, though there can be a delay of several days. Clumps of eggs, dyed black with ink and known as "sea grapes", can be seen attached to seaweed or eelgrass in the summer months (top photograph, opposite page). The eggs hatch after two to three months and miniature cuttlefish, around finger-nail size, emerge (middle photograph, opposite page). As mentioned earlier, the junior cuttlefish immediately show good powers of patterning control. Even so, they are very vulnerable to predators, and mortality at this stage in their life is high. Females only breed once and die soon after

Common cuttlefish - *Sepia officinalis*

laying their eggs. Unlike their relative the octopus, they take no care of them. After cuttlefish have died and decomposed, their internal skeleton or cuttlebone (bottom photograph, this page) is often found washed up on beaches. In life, this is the animal's buoyancy organ and it consists of stacks of thin-walled chambers that can be filled with either liquid or gas in order to give precisely the right degree of lift. Cuttlefish spend the winter in relatively deep water, such as that in the Western English Channel, though they cannot inhabit very deep water because the cuttlebone could implode under high pressure. They move into shallow coastal waters, all around the South West, to breed in the spring and summer. It is then that divers can see them in large numbers, and snorkellers may even see them close to the shore. Numbers of cuttlefish seen inshore at particular locations fluctuate markedly, with large numbers being seen in some years and hardly any in others. Cuttlefish are impressive predators, able to catch fast moving prey such as fish or prawns with their long tentacles. The arms, along with the razor-sharp beak hidden behind them,

Cuttlefish eggs

A new hatchling

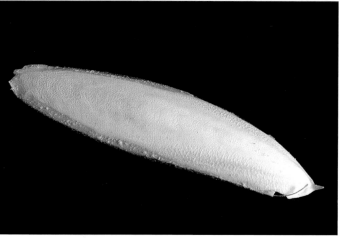
Cuttlebone

Common cuttlefish - *Sepia officinalis*

Familiar gesture by cornered cuttlefish

also enable a pugnacious crab to be turned into a meal in seconds. If a cuttlefish's approach is met by a crab with defiantly raised claws, it will simply grab it from the rear. Aside from sea mammals, cuttlefish are undoubtedly the most intelligent creatures a diver will meet. Encounters leave you with the impression that you have been observed as much as observing! The individual being watched in the photograph above has extended its two long tentacles, a gesture sometimes seen in situations when a cuttlefish might feel cornered. Is it an attempt at communication? [Up to 30 cm long]

Little cuttle - *Sepiola atlantica*

The little cuttle, *Sepiola*, has the appearance of a miniature *Sepia*. It is very difficult to spot underwater and only close inspection will reveal that it is a rather different shape to its larger relative. The body is cup-shaped and there is a pair of lobe-like fins that do not run the entire length of the body. Other characteristic features include its very protrusive eyes and the greenish tinge to the tops of the eye bulges. The little cuttle's buoyancy control system is less sophisticated than that of the common cuttlefish but it can hover effectively or jet away quickly. The tiny clouds of ink released by this species when disturbed appear quite comical to the diver, but can still be used effectively in combination with colour control. By discharging a dark cloud of ink at the same moment that they jet away, and by turning their body from dark to pale, a predator's attention can be distracted to follow the ink cloud and the cuttle can escape unnoticed. The photograph above shows the role of individual colour cells (chromatophores) in cuttlefish pattern control. In the middle of the body, the cells are expanded forming dark discs. In the near part of the rear, they are contracted into small spots so the skin appears mainly white. Little cuttles live on sandy bottoms and spend much of the time partly buried with only their eyes exposed, watching for predators or hapless small crustaceans which they will capture on emerging from the sand. [Up to 5 cm long]

Chapter 7

ECHINODERMS

Starfish, brittle stars, sea urchins, sea cucumbers & feather stars

The name, echinoderm, means "spiny-skinned" and refers to the skeleton of these animals, which is composed of bony plates embedded in the body wall. These plates may protrude to form spines and take on very different forms in the various sub-groups. They are relatively loosely arranged in starfish for instance, but form a rigid structure in sea urchins. Echinoderms have no front or back end because they are based on what is called radial symmetry, rather than the bilateral symmetry of many familiar animals. Starfish, for instance, are just as likely to lead with one arm as with any other, and have no need to turn their body when changing direction. Some urchins and sea cucumbers operate as though they have a front end, but their basic body plan is still based on radial symmetry. Most echinoderms have separate sexes (rather than being hermaphrodites) and release their eggs and sperm into the water, so that fertilisation is external. A planktonic larval phase usually follows, and the larvae go through different stages before becoming miniature adults and settling on the sea bed.

Starfish features

The first thing you notice if you turn a starfish over is the huge number of tiny extendable legs, known as tube feet, bursting from the groove underneath each arm. All echinoderms have tube feet, operated by a special hydraulic system, even though they may be less conspicuous than those of starfish. Starfish tube feet are usually equipped with small suckers for gripping onto firm surfaces, and are used for walking the animal along and, in some species, for pulling open prey (see pages 88-89). The close-up photograph on the opposite page shows the tube feet underneath the arm of a spiny starfish. It also shows the upper side of the arm, on which the prominent spines are surrounded by bunches of tiny structures, called pedicellariae, that have an intriguing function. Slow moving animals with a hard exterior can present an ideal home for encrusting animals, such as barnacles, looking for a free ride. The pedicellariae are like miniature pairs of jaws which, when touched by a small animal looking for somewhere to settle, will grasp it and kill it. Starfish have amazing regenerative powers. A single detached arm can produce a whole new starfish, as long as part of the central body is also present. This explains the bizarre shape of some individuals.

Brittle stars

These animals look like emaciated starfish but have a different body layout because their arms are very clearly demarcated from the central disc. The bony plates of the arms form a continuous articulated armour which gives the whole arm the appearance

Starfish close-up, showing tube feet, spines and pedicellariae

of having joints. The arms are easily broken, hence the name, and can be jettisoned to permit escape from a predator, and then regenerated. Brittle stars move much more rapidly than starfish, using snake like movements of their arms to propel them across the sea bed. The tube feet simply give the arm some grip, rather than walking the animal along.

Sea urchins

The bony plates possessed by sea urchins are more imposing than those of any other echinoderms and fit together to form a solid structure, known as a test. The usually impressive spines are mobile, being attached to the test with ball-and-socket joints, and they can help the tube feet with movement or be locked rigidly in position to anchor the urchin in a rock crevice. The tube feet are similar to those of starfish, though they need to be much longer to reach out beyond the spines.

Sea cucumbers

These cucumber-shaped animals can be visualised

as starfish with no arms that have grown extremely tall and thin. Some sea cucumbers, like the cotton-spinner, crawl over the bottom eating organic deposits. Others wedge themselves into rock crevices or burrow into soft sediments. From here, they hold out feeding tentacles, which are highly modified tube feet that surround their mouths, to catch suspended food. More conventional tube feet along the rest of the body help the cucumber with walking or burrowing. The skeleton of sea cucumbers is simply a few scattered bony elements in their leathery skin. As with other echinoderms however, the soft elements of the body wall can alter consistency, being soft when the cucumber needs to get through a narrow crack and then stiff when it needs to wedge itself in position.

Feather stars

The aptly named feather stars have a long fossil history and are thought to be the most primitive echinoderms. The typical feather star features are described on page 98.

Common starfish - *Asterias rubens*

The most familiar starfish to non-divers, it can be found on the lower shore and at virtually any depth, on sandy and stony sea beds as well as on rocks. It is usually orange or pale yellow/brown, sometimes red or purple, with a cream underside. The five (occasionally four or six) arms taper down towards their tips. The starfish's upper surface is covered with small blunt spines, with a marked line of larger spines down the middle of each arm. Belying their sluggish image, these starfish can be fearsome predators of bivalve molluscs such as mussels and clams. The top photograph, opposite, shows a starfish in characteristic feeding pose arched over a clam (the stripes on its shell are just discernible). In using this position, it puts the maximum number of tube feet to work on pulling open the mollusc, and also positions its mouth right next to the crack between the shell halves. It is not clear whether a steady pull or a series of tugs is used, but the force applied by the tube feet has been estimated as being equivalent to 5 kg, and the hapless mollusc eventually tires. As soon as the tiniest crack appears between the shell halves, as little as one tenth of a millimetre, the starfish pushes its stomach out through its mouth and slips it through the crack into the mollusc's interior. Digestive juices get to work and the battle is over. Starfish can be serious pests to mussel or oyster fisheries. Past attempts to kill dredged up starfish by simply chopping them in half and throwing them back into the sea were doomed to failure, because each half starfish simply grew another half and carried on as before! The bottom photograph, opposite, shows how a starfish can right itself by twisting its arms and pulling itself over with the versatile tube feet. [Up to 50 cm across but rarely more than 30 cm and usually smaller]

Common starfish - *Asterias rubens*

Feeding on a clam

Righting itself

Spiny starfish - *Marthasterias glacialis*

With its large body covered in conspicuous knobs and spines, the spiny starfish can be an impressive animal. It is very common in West Country waters and in many shallow rocky bays it appears much more numerous than the so-called common starfish. In the meadows of red seaweed, their usual pale blue colouration makes them extremely easy to spot. They can also be grey, brown or white, the purple tips to the arms being most noticeable on white individuals. Although the arms of this species appear heavily armoured with three rows of large spines running their length, they are quite soft and will be readily jettisoned if hurt or over-handled. Fortunately, they can be regenerated and spiny starfish with a mixture of normal arms and smaller ones in the process of being re-grown are a common sight. The tiny pincer-like organs, pedicellariae, are particularly prominent in this species and form obvious cushion-like wreaths around the large spines. Spiny starfish are voracious predators and, in addition to preying on bivalve molluscs, eat crustaceans, fish and other echinoderms such as starfish and sea urchins, dead or alive. [Up to 80 cm across but usually much smaller]

Bloody Henry - *Henricia oculata*

Common in shallow rocky areas, the bloody Henry has an upper side that is usually coloured a dramatic pink, purple or crimson, and which has a rough sandpaper-like texture. The underside is a pale sandy colour. It has quite a different appearance from the common and spiny starfish, because its five arms are round in

cross-section, lack any obvious spines and look stiffer than those of the other species. It is a suspension feeder for at least some of the time, raising its arms up to catch food particles, and also browses on sponges. It has a smaller stomach than the more predatory starfish. [Up to 20 cm across]

Cushion star - *Asterina gibbosa*

The relatively large central portion and short blunt arms of the cushion star give it a distinctive, almost pentagonal shape. It is usually much smaller than the other starfish described here, and is mainly found on the shore or in very shallow water. The upper surface of its body is rough, covered in small bundles of short spines. These spines, and those

around the edges of the arms, are usually orange but the overall colour is quite variable, ranging from green or brown through to cream. Cushion stars start out as males and become females later in life. Most starfish have entirely separate sexes. [Up to 5 cm across]

Seven armed starfish - *Luidia ciliaris*

A relatively primitive starfish, *Luidia* has a distinctive appearance, although its orange colouration is shared by other species. The seven long arms are rather soft and only start to taper near their tips. A very prominent fringe of white spines runs round the edge of each arm. Unlike the majority of starfish, its tube feet end in tiny knobs rather than suckers. *Luidia* is found on both sandy and stony sea beds where it can move surprisingly quickly, feeding mainly on other echinoderms such as brittle stars, starfish and urchins. An adult can apparently produce over two hundred million eggs in a year, so mortality at the egg and planktonic larval stages must be enormous. [Up to 60 cm across]

Sand star - *Astropecten irregularis*

This burrowing species has a classic star shape with five rigid arms that taper noticeably along their entire length. Each arm is fringed with long pale spines and normally has a purple spot at its tip. The overall colour is typically a pinkish sandy hue though this may vary. With a much more flattened body than most starfish, and with spiked instead of sucker-bearing tube feet, the sand star is well adapted for burrowing into soft sediments, though it may emerge from time to time. While burrowing, it is thought to eat shellfish, crustaceans and worms encountered along the way. It may even take small fish if they are slowed down by ill health. [Up to 15 cm across]

Common brittle star - *Ophiothrix fragilis*

This brittle star has flexible and very bristly arms, with the central body also bearing spines. Colouration is very variable but the arms almost always have alternating light and dark bands. It is usually seen on rocky sea beds or underneath stones and can sometimes be found forming huge aggregations in deep water. Within these, up to 10,000 brittle stars per square metre have been recorded. The brittle star's arms can be raised up into the passing current where their tube feet filter out suspended food matter, which is then passed along the arms to the mouth. They also eat organic debris on the sea bed. [Up to 20 cm across]

Sand brittle star - *Ophiura ophiura*

Normally found on sand or muddy sand, this species has a relatively large disc and shorter, stiffer arms than many brittle stars. Its arms are much less bristly than the common brittle star and it is also less colourful, usually being a drab sandy brown. There may be an attractive pattern on the central body, however, created by the plates which cover its surface. The sand brittle star can burrow into the sediment or move quite quickly across its surface by using its arms in a "swimming" or "rowing" motion. The animal at the top right of the photograph is a burrowing anemone (see page 32). [Up to 25 cm across but usually much smaller]

Common (or edible) sea urchin - *Echinus esculentus*

Close-up of common sea urchin, showing tube feet, spines and pedicellariae

Common (or edible) sea urchin - *Echinus esculentus*

The skeleton (also known as a test) of this impressive animal is very rounded and is usually bright red, though the numerous white spine attachment points tend to make it appear pink. Some individuals, as in the photograph, have a fetching purple hue. The abundant spines are strong, but quite short and thin relative to the overall body size in comparison to other urchins. The bottom photograph is an extreme close-up of an urchin's surface and it shows how the features are very similar to those of a starfish, all be it with different proportions. The spines are of similar form and the tube feet (top left and lower edge of picture) are almost identical, though of course longer in order to reach out beyond the spines when help with anchoring or movement is required. The pincer-like pedicellariae for removing "free-loaders" have long stems and are particularly noticeable. Without them, the slow-moving urchin would have even more trouble with accumulating debris and unwanted guests than would the relatively (!) athletic starfish. Urchins are powerful and omnivorous grazers, eating animals such as barnacles in addition to algae, and are capable of leaving virtually bare swathes across a rock face. They can therefore form an important component of the ecology in rocky areas. Rock-dwelling urchins such as *Echinus* have a feeding mechanism known as Aristotle's lantern (it was he who first described it), which consists of a complex structure of plates and muscles that supports five chisel-like teeth used for scraping food from surfaces. This species is much more common in Cornwall than in Devon or Dorset. [Up to 20 cm across]

Common heart urchin (or sea potato) - *Echinocardium cordatum*

Though very abundant, heart urchins are seldom seen because they burrow into a sandy sea bed and spend most of their time 10 to 15 cm beneath its surface. The individual shown here was found on the surface of the sand at Torquay. Unlike the common sea urchin, the test (skeleton) is not round but oval, a shape better suited to the burrowing lifestyle. It also means there is a front and back end. Dense yellow/gold spines cover the test and all point backwards, giving the animal a furry appearance. The spines are used for burrowing, especially the ones shaped like spatulas on the under-surface. Heart

urchins construct a channel that runs up to the surface of the sand where it forms a small but noticeable depression. Special, highly elongated tube feet stretch up the channel and are used for respiration and for collecting the deposited particles on which the urchin feeds. Unlike urchins that are crunching grazers, heart urchins possess no Aristotle's lantern. A type of small bivalve mollusc is often found living in association with this species. [Up to 10 cm long]

Cotton-spinner - *Holothuria forskali*

This large sausage-shaped sea cucumber is typically found crawling slowly over exposed rocks. The overall colour is usually black, but the yellow or pale brown on its underside may sometimes spread up over the rest of the body. Most of the body is covered with conical protuberances, except for the flatter underside which bears the tube feet used for locomotion. These features are reminders that you are looking at a relative of the starfish, rather than an exceptionally well fed and prickly slug! The cotton-spinner has short tentacles, rather than the long feathery ones of suspension-feeding sea cucumbers (opposite), and consumes silty deposits from the sea bed. Having extracted the nutritious organic component, it leaves distinctive trails of undigested material that look like strings of large

Defences activated

sandy beads. The name cotton-spinner comes from the animal's habit of producing long white threads from its rear end if molested (see smaller photograph). The threads are part of its internal organs and are extremely sticky, serving to confuse or entangle the attacker. [Up to 25 cm long]

Brown sea cucumber - *Aslia lefevrei*

The brown, leathery gherkin-shaped body of this animal is generally hidden in a rock crevice, but its large and highly branched tentacles extend out into open water. The tentacles are dark brown with some white edging often present. Mucus on the tentacles collects suspended matter, and each tentacle is in turn rolled up and inserted into the central mouth so that

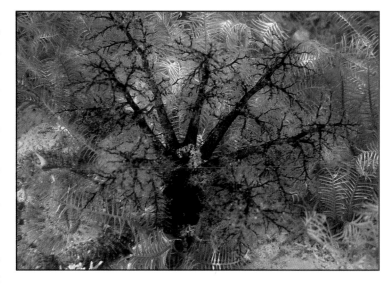

the food can be collected (see arm at "five o'clock" position), before it is then re-extended. It is very difficult to watch this process without visualising a child gradually sucking jam from their sticky fingers. The cucumber in the photograph is surrounded by feather stars (page 98) and daisy anemones (page 25). [Tentacles up to 10 cm long]

Gravel sea cucumber - *Neopentadactyla mixta*

This sea cucumber has feathery white feeding tentacles which are extended above the gravel sea bed in which it lives. The tentacles are attractively decorated with brown flecks which can be so dense that the overall colour becomes brown. There may also be striking brown and white patterns around the mouth. A small portion of the long, tapering body may be visible but the majority of

its length is buried and hidden from view. If disturbed, the tentacles can be rapidly withdrawn, though individuals seem to vary greatly in their sensitivity. Like so many animals that rely on suspended food, they like areas with good water movement. [Tentacles up to 15 cm long]

Feather star - *Antedon bifida*

This abundant animal has ten feathery arms of variable colour, though often red and white, while the overall pattern can produce a mottled or freckled appearance. On the underside of the body, there are twenty-five or so shorter claw-like appendages, used for anchoring the feather star to the sea bed, to kelp stems or to sponges (as in the photograph). Their grip is surprisingly tenacious, as divers who have found them clinging to equipment will know. Feather stars can swim by sweeping their arms up and down, or by crawling slowly on the tips of the arms which are bent right over to hold the body away from the sea bed. They spend the vast majority of their time, however, simply anchored in their chosen location where they engage in suspension feeding. The arms and their feathery branches are equipped with numerous tiny tube feet that catch floating food and flick it into grooves which run down each arm. This food is then transported by the beating action of tiny hairs down to the mouth in the centre of the body. Unlike starfish, urchins and brittle stars, feather stars have their mouth on the top side of their body. When not being used for either feeding or locomotion, the arms can be curled up over the body. Though often found singly or in small groups, feather stars are most noticeable when they form huge aggregations. These are most common in current-swept areas not exposed to heavy surf. [Up to 15 cm across]

Chapter 8
SEA SQUIRTS

Unlikely relatives

The sea squirts are a most deceptive group of animals. By living sedentary lives, and feeding by filtering plankton and other food particles from seawater, they appear similar to more primitive creatures such as the sponges. Amazingly, sea squirts are members of the phylum Chordata, the major animal group that contains such creatures as fish, birds and ourselves. The adult sea squirt gives little indication of this elevated status, but the tiny sea squirt larva resembles a tadpole and possesses a very simplified version of the backbone and nerve chord that are characteristic of its advanced relatives.

Larval secrets

Sea squirt eggs are released into the sea or brooded by the adult, depending on the species. When the larvae, or tadpoles, first hatch from eggs, they swim up towards the light. This is made possible by a light receptor (primitive eye) and a muscular tail which works well because of the stiffening provided by the rudimentary backbone (known as a notochord). Soon however, the larvae's behaviour changes, and they swim away from the light and down towards the sea bed. Here, they attach themselves to a suitable substrate with adhesive pads on their front end, and completely lose their youthful mobility. The tail is reabsorbed, most of their more sophisticated features such as the notochord disappear, and an adult sea squirt results. Many species form colonies.

The adult form

The adult body is, in essence, a U-shaped tube surrounded by a tough and leathery tunic (this is why sea squirts are also known as tunicates). There is an efficient filtration and pumping system in the centre of the tube, based on the action of numerous beating cilia (tiny hair-like structures). The tube's ends are clearly visible as two openings or siphons: one for the intake of water and one for its expulsion. If a sea squirt is disturbed it can contract its body and water is squirted from the two siphons (hence the name). The body contains an intestine for processing the filtered material and a strange blood circulation system that is unique to sea squirts. Blood is pumped one way round the body for several seconds and the flow is then reversed for an equivalent length of time. Sea squirts are preyed upon by a variety of animals. Sea slugs, in particular, are often seen munching through colonies. Some species protect themselves by having a highly acidic body wall which renders them unpalatable.

Light bulb sea squirt - *Clavelina lepadiformis*

These attractive sea squirts live in bunches that may contain a few or dozens of individuals. The transparent tunic with its delicate yellow or white markings, and the visible internal organs, give the animal its name. Although a colonial species, individuals are free along most of their length and are joined to each other only at their base. The reddish eggs and developing larvae can sometimes be seen within the body cavity. The larvae are released in the late summer and the individual squirts then regress to leave "buds" which survive through the winter and develop into new squirts in the spring. [Up to 2 cm tall. Clumps up to 15 cm across are quite common]

Aplidium punctum

This sea squirt forms close-knit colonies where individuals are barely distinguishable from each other. Each colony appears to have a bulbous head on a thinner stalk, and contains approximately forty or more individuals. Close examination reveals that each individual is marked with a tiny dark orange spot that stands out against the generally whitish head. Several colonies are often bunched

close together (as shown here), attached to rocks, stones or seaweed. The stalks of the colonies are fairly pale. Colonies of a very similar species, *Morchellium argus*, are more reddish in colour and have red stalks. [Colonies, including stalk, up to 4 cm long]

Phallusia mammillata

The largest British sea squirt and a truly solitary species. The West Country represents the northern extent of its distribution and it is usually only seen in sheltered locations such as Torbay and Portland harbour. It is rather plump in appearance and the milk-white or yellowish tunic is unusually thick for a sea squirt and appears quite stiff. Its body surface is covered with rounded, smooth swellings (hence

mammillata). The water intake siphon is at the very top of the body, the outlet part-way down. Small anemones sometimes live on this sea squirt, taking the opportunity to get away from bottom silt and receive better access to passing food. [Up to 15 cm tall]

Gooseberry sea squirt - *Dendrodoa grossularia*

This species is defined as solitary because it can live alone, but it is most likely to be seen in aggregations on the walls of rock gullies, under overhangs or on stones. Such groups result from the settling larvae's gregarious behaviour, rather than from budding. The squirts' usual colour is a cherry or orangey red and individuals are normally very rounded in shape and almost dome-like, though some may appear more upright and cylindrical in form. The two protruding siphons are well separated. This species is readily consumed by predatory sea slugs which can sometimes be found chewing their way hungrily through the aggregations. [Up to 2 cm tall]

Leathery sea squirt - *Styela clava*

A tall sea squirt whose stalk gives it a distinctive club-like shape, although the stalk itself can be hidden by creatures living nearby. Its blotchy brown surface has a slightly "padded quilt-like" appearance and the two siphons, which can bear broad stripes, are right at its top end. It is found singly or in small groups, the photograph shows a row of squirts surrounded by feather stars (page 98). *Styela clava* is actually a native of the Pacific Ocean and is thought to have been brought to our shores on the hulls of ships. Very common in Plymouth Sound, though a covering of encrusting growths sometimes make it unrecognisable. [Up to 12 cm tall]

Star sea squirt - *Botryllus schlosseri*

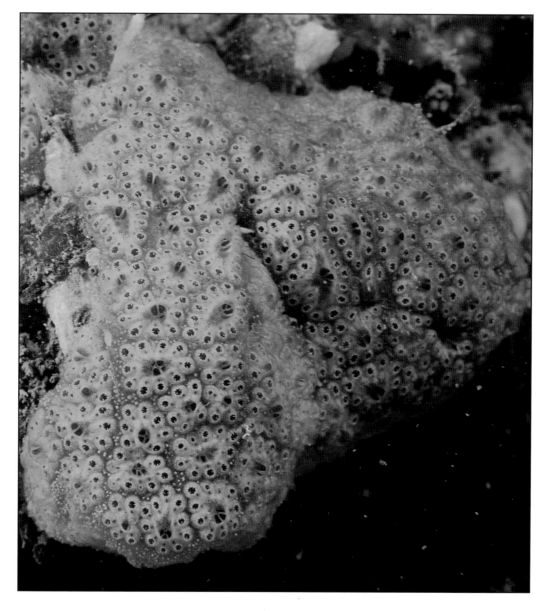

Colonies of star squirts are so closely organised that they bear hardly any resemblance to the standard sea squirt form. A colony resides in a common gelatinous tunic, while groups of three to twelve individuals within the colony each produce one of the characteristic star-shaped patterns that cover its surface. Within these groups, the individuals have separate intake siphons but share a common outflow opening in the centre of the star. The basic tunic is usually a dark colour while the stars are a contrasting yellow. Colonies may appear flat or bulbous in their overall shape and are found encrusting rocks and seaweed. Reproduction can be sexual or achieved by budding. [Colonies around 10 cm across are common]

Chapter 9

FISH

One of the most enjoyable aspects of diving in West Country waters is the large number and variety of fish to be seen, even during a single dive or snorkelling session. While the classic fish shape is represented by species such as bass, grey mullet and pollack, many of the other fish seen in shallow water have different shapes which reflect their bottom-dwelling existence. Adaptations to this lifestyle can include a flattened and enlarged head, with upward-facing mouth, like sea scorpions and angler fish. Such fish spend a great deal of time lying stationary on the sea bed, relying on camouflage to avoid predators and enable them to ambush their prey. Other species have become highly elongated so they can hide amongst sea weed (pipefish) or slip into the narrowest of crevices (conger eels). Still others have thin plate-like bodies, staying upright to sneak up on their prey (John Dory) or lying on their sides on the sea bed (plaice, sole).

Fins: their layout and function

Despite the variety in fish body shape, it is quite easy to see that all the various species conform to the same basic plan. A good clue is the fins which, despite unusual appearances or adaptations to different functions, are generally laid out in the same pattern (see below). The tail fin provides propulsion and acts as a rudder, while the dorsal and anal fins help with stability by preventing body roll and also act as pivots when the fish is turning. They are known as the

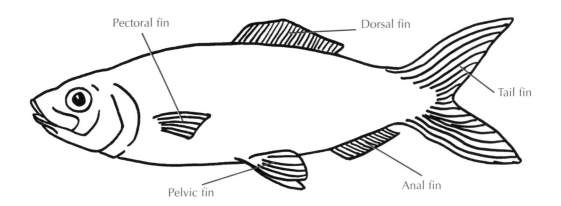

Pectoral fin

Dorsal fin

Tail fin

Pelvic fin

Anal fin

unpaired fins though there may be one, two or even three dorsal fins. The paired fins, pectoral and pelvic, correspond (as their names imply) to the front and hind limbs of land-living vertebrate animals such as ourselves. Pectoral fins are used to help with all sorts of manoeuvres such as turning, braking, rising and falling. The pelvic fins vary considerably in their position from one species to another; they tend to help the pectorals with manoeuvrability and maintaining stability. In addition to these basic functions, fins may be used for catching food, repelling predators, mating, courtship display and assisting with camouflage.

Varied approaches to breeding

Many open sea fish take virtually no care of their young and adopt a "squirt and hope" strategy. A male and female shed vast numbers of eggs and sperm into the water near each other, and seem to make little effort to ensure that fertilisation occurs. Parental attention thereafter is non-existent, and the developing embryos are left entirely to their own devices amongst the plankton in open water. It's not that the parents "don't care", it's simply that they put their energy and resources into quantity rather than quality. Such resources can be substantial, as demonstrated by the weakened state of many fish after breeding. In some species that use this strategy, adults die immediately after their one and only spawning. Many of the shallow water fish familiar to divers use an alternative approach to "squirt and hope". They produce far fewer eggs and make much more strenuous efforts to ensure fertilisation and the survival of the resulting young. It seems that a strategy suited to the open sea is less successful in coastal waters where predators are more numerous and physical conditions are harsher. Abandoned eggs and larvae could easily be washed into less suitable

habitats such as estuaries or deeper water. Interestingly, it is very often the male of common coastal species that takes on the main burden of parenthood. Their nest-building and egg-guarding activities make an interesting spectacle for the observant diver.

Skeletons of bone or cartilage

The major division in the fish world is that between those with skeletons made entirely from cartilage (sharks and rays) and those with bony skeletons (all the rest). The cartilaginous fish have other characteristic features, such as exposed gill slits and skin covered with tooth-like scales. Their fins are much thicker and more fleshy than those of bony fish, and may also be used slightly differently. The pectoral fins are usually large and, because a buoyancy organ is lacking, act as hydroplanes to provide lift for swimming. Rays have taken this to the extreme and have huge pectoral fins used as wings. Despite these differences, however, the sharks and rays share the same basic fin layout already described. The bony fish have complex and hardened skeletons, similar to those of other vertebrates like ourselves, and their thinner fins are supported by fin rays. They are far more numerous than the cartilaginous fish, with over twenty thousand species versus seven hundred or so. An important characteristic of bony fish is their more sophisticated buoyancy control system, that uses an adjustable gas-filled organ called a swimbladder. By adding or removing gas from the swimbladder, in a similar way to a diver using a buoyancy compensator, neutral buoyancy can be achieved so that energy is concentrated solely on forward motion. However, many of the bony fish species that live on the sea bed, such as blennies and flatfish for example, do not actually need this facility and have lost their swimbladders.

Lesser spotted dogfish - *Scyliorhinus canicula*

Dogfish are in essence small sharks, and this species is much the most common fish of this type encountered by divers off South West coasts. It has shark-like characteristics such as a mouth positioned on the underside of the head, and obvious gill slits just in front of the hydroplane-like pectoral fins. The dorsal fins are small, rounded and positioned well back on the body, however, and thus bear little resemblance to those of the larger sharks. The body is a greyish brown in colour with numerous dark spots, and a white belly. Tooth-like scales that cover the dogfish have spines that point backwards. The skin, once used as sandpaper, feels quite smooth if stroked from nose to tail and very rough in the opposite direction. Dogfish are often seen "snoozing" on the sea bed during the day, sometimes in pairs (opposite page, top photograph) or even in groups. They hunt at night, feeding on crabs, whelks and bottom-living fish such as gobies, dabs and gurnards. Dogfish seem to rely heavily on their sense of smell when hunting and may slavishly follow a scent trail, even when their prey has turned and swum right back past them. They can also detect faint electrical fields produced by the muscles of hidden prey. After mating in the autumn, the female comes inshore during the winter or spring to lay her distinctive brown egg capsules, known as "mermaids' purses". These have long tendrils on the corners and, as they are laid, the mother fish will swim round and round a clump of seaweed or similar anchorage, so that they become well attached (opposite page, bottom photograph). Each capsule contains a single embryo and a miniature dogfish emerges after nine months or so. [Fish up to 80 cm long, egg cases are about 7 cm long]

Lesser spotted dogfish - *Scyliorhinus canicula*

A "snoozing" pair

Egg case

Thornback ray - *Raja clavata*

The thornback is the most commonly encountered ray in the South West, often being found in relatively deep water such as the bottom of Plymouth Sound, but also in very shallow areas such as the Helford estuary where this one was photographed. It is usually a blotchy brown or grey and, as the name suggests, bears an array of large thorn-like projections on its back and tail. Some "thorns" have an obvious plate-like base. Rays and skates belong to the same group of fish as sharks and dogfish and, similarly, have a skeleton made of cartilage rather than hard bone. With their flat diamond-shaped bodies, rays can be thought of as "squashed sharks". The greatly enlarged pectoral fins form the "wings" which give them a wonderfully graceful flying motion when swimming. Like most rays, the thornback spends much of its time lying motionless on the sea bed where its body shape, along with the habit of covering itself in sand, makes it very difficult to spot. Fish usually take in water for breathing through their mouths, but rays can use the breathing holes (spiracles) behind the eyes on top of their head; they thus avoid taking in too much sand. Like the dogfish, the thornback ray lays its eggs as "mermaid's purses" but these are black rather than brown. It feeds on a variety of bottom-living animals, especially crabs and shrimps. [Up to 1 m long]

Conger eel - *Conger conger*

The Latin name is uniquely memorable and its owner is pretty unforgettable too. It is a highly elongated fish with a powerful snake-like body, grey-brown to grey-blue in colour with a paler underside. There are no scales and its skin is smooth. The dorsal, tail and anal fins are merged to form a single fringe that runs from just behind the head, right round the pointed tail, to underneath the belly. Congers hide in rocky holes and crevices however, so it is usually only the head that is seen, with its large mouth and distinctive snout bearing a pair of tubular nostrils. Shipwrecks, with all their nooks and crannies, are popular residences. Congers are formidable predators and will slip out of their lair at night to hunt fish, including smaller congers, and large crustaceans such as crabs and lobsters. The latter are seized and may be battered against rocks before being swallowed. Surprisingly, this doesn't seem to stop lobsters and prawns often sharing the crevices that congers use as home. Congers do not breed in our coastal waters but travel vast distances to spawn in the deep mid-Atlantic. Their bodies change as they approach the breeding grounds with teeth falling out, gut degenerating and the gonads becoming so greatly enlarged that they make up a third of body weight. They die after spawning and their larvae drift back into coastal waters and then turn into young eels. Congers have incredibly strong jaws and a reputation for ferocity but remain docile underwater unless provoked, so anglers have more to fear than divers. [Up to 2 m long and occasionally even larger]

Angler fish - *Lophius piscatorius*

This very unusual fish, gastronomically known as a monkfish, is superbly adapted to its habitat and lifestyle so, considering its potential size, it can be surprisingly difficult to spot. The whole body is flattened, particularly the enormous broad head, and the tail appears small by comparison. Overall body colour is usually brown or greenish-brown with a white underside. Lying on the bottom, its mottled pattern gives good camouflage and the outline is further broken up by the fringe of small flaps of skin round the base of the head. The angler's name, of course, stems from its cunning means of attracting food. The foremost spiny ray of its dorsal fin is separate from the rest of the fin and serves as a "fishing rod". This "rod" can be moved around and the fleshy tip acts as a lure, inviting inquisitive creatures perilously close to the huge upturned mouth. The prey is then engulfed, a process aided by the inrush of water as the angler opens its jaws. Large inward-curving teeth make escape impossible. All sorts of bottom-living fish (including flatfish, gurnards, rays and conger eels) and other animals are eaten, even diving birds. The angler fish spawns in very deep water, laying its eggs in sheets which can form huge rafts up to 10 metres long and have occasionally been mistaken for sea monsters. A sheet typically contains around a million eggs. Hatchlings live freely in open water until they are around 8 cm long, and then take up life on the sea bed. Extra-long fins help keep the youngsters afloat, but these have receded by the time the fish come to settle. [Up to 2 m long but it is much smaller individuals that are usually seen]

Pollack - *Pollachius pollachius*

Adult

Seen either singly or in shoals, the pollack is a very common fish in West Country waters and will be seen on virtually every dive over shallow rocky ground in the summer months. The pollack is a member of the cod family and conforms to their typical pattern of three dorsal and two anal fins. Adults (main photograph) are generally dark green along the back and more silvery on the sides and belly. The lateral line is usually obvious and curves upwards by the pectoral fins. Juveniles, which can often be seen very close to the shore, are more darkly coloured in green or brown and some may even be a fetching crimson and gold (smaller photograph). With only a little patience, adult pollack can be watched feeding on sand eels (page 120). Hunting individually or in small groups, they will lurk close to the sea bed, gazing watchfully at the sand eel shoal swirling above them. Suddenly darting up through the

Juvenile

shoal, they will grab any unwary fish before returning to near the bottom and waiting for the shoal to re-group. Juveniles can be seen using an identical technique on groups of mysid shrimps or two-spot gobies (page 133). [Usually up to around 50 cm long, larger fish sometimes seen near wrecks. Juvenile shown here about 8 cm]

Bib - *Trisopterus luscus*

The bib is another common member of the cod family. Its body has quite a deep shape and is coppery coloured with an attractive banding that is usually, but not always, visible. There is a dark spot at the base of each pectoral fin. A single barbel underneath the chin is a useful distinguishing feature, and the upper jaw protrudes slightly in contrast to the jutting lower jaw of the pollack. Bib are frequently seen inside and near wrecks in small groups. Large shoals of very small bib, often found over the sand near wrecks, will approach and even surround the diver whilst in search of any small pieces of food stirred up from the bottom. [Up to 50 cm long but usually no more than 30 cm]

Poor-cod - *Trisopterus minutus*

Belonging to the same genus as the bib, the poor cod is a close relative and possesses a very similar appearance. It shares features such as the protruding upper jaw and the long barbel on the lower. The poor cod can be distinguished from the bib by its shallower body shape, lack of banding and generally smaller size. It may be seen individually or in quite large groups. Shoals of small fish seen near wrecks are often a mixture of both bib and poor cod. [Up to 25 cm long]

John Dory - *Zeus faber*

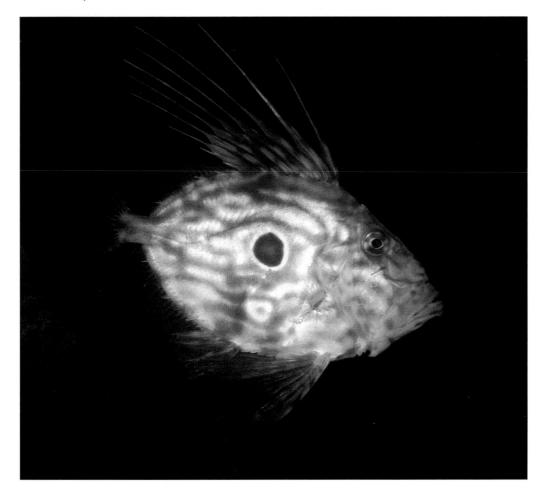

A highly distinctive fish, the John Dory has a body shaped like a flat oval plate on edge. Other notable features are the large head with its mournful expression, the very long dorsal fin rays and a single dark spot in the centre of each flank. The thin body virtually disappears when viewed head-on or tail-on, a characteristic used to good effect when approaching unsuspecting prey or avoiding predators. While not a rapid mover, the John Dory shows great manoeuvrability when stalking its prey, swimming while tilted at all sorts of angles and even upside down. At the same time, stripes on its flanks can alternately recede and intensify which, when coupled with the thin outline, makes its approach even harder to spot. Its jaws have a special bone construction which makes them highly protrusible. Once close to its unsuspecting prey, the mouth shoots out to engulf the victim. Prey is usually small fish such as sand-eels, herring and pilchards. In the shallow water where encounters with divers tend to occur, they are often seen hunting the two-spot gobies (page 133) that hover in patches of sea weed. Legend has it that the dark blotches on each flank are St Peter's fingerprints, left when he took a coin from the fish's mouth to pay his tax. [Up to 60 cm long but usually much smaller]

Greater pipefish - *Syngnathus acus*

Pipefish look very much like straightened and elongated sea horses, which are in fact their close relatives. Pipefish are like sea horses in having no scales. They have a series of jointed, bone-like rings which encircle the body from just behind the head down to the tail, giving most species a rather rigid, armoured appearance. The small mouth is positioned at the end of a slender snout and is used to suck in the tiny animals on which pipefish feed. Pipefish may move around by using a snake-like body action or, like sea horses, by rapid fluttering movements of their fins. The characteristic features of *Syngnathus acus* are its rough body with angular cross section, the very long snout taking up more than half the total length of the head and the bump on top of the head behind the eyes. It is

usually found amongst seaweed or eel-grass where its shape and colour provide effective camouflage. The fish species of shallow water generally give their eggs good care, but pipefish take this to the extreme. The female lays her eggs into a special brood pouch on the belly of the male, where the young develop until emerging as miniature adults. [Up to 50 cm long]

Snake pipefish - *Entelurus aequoreus*

The snake pipefish is easily distinguished by its striking colouration of orange-brown with thin but clearly defined pale hoops. There is also a fetching dark stripe running back through the eye. Aside from the colour, it is also rather different in form to the greater pipefish and similar species. The body is much smoother and more rounded in cross section, so it does not appear armoured. There are also no pectoral fins and the tail fin is virtually non-existent (see smaller photograph), so the overall effect is certainly snake-like. Snake pipefish are often found using their tail curled round seaweed as an anchor, while they swing round sucking in their food of tiny floating animals. Rather than having a special brood pouch like that of other pipefish, the male snake

Tail used as anchor

pipefish carries the eggs in a simpler hollow on the outside of its belly. [At up to 60 cm long, this species is our largest pipefish]

Long-spined sea scorpion - *Taurulus bubalis*

The long-spined sea scorpion, sometimes simply referred to as the sea scorpion, is a common fish of shallow water and surprisingly large individuals can even be found in rockpools. The first part of its name comes from the long sturdy spine pointing backwards from each gill cover. There are also some smaller spines nearby but none are venomous, unlike those of the Mediterranean scorpion fish. A distinctive little barbel is visible at either corner of the mouth. The broad head has bony crests and there are no scales but, instead, bony plates embedded in the skin. The sea scorpion's irregular outline and mottled patterning is only part of its camouflage story, for it has an impressive ability to replicate the colour of its surroundings. It will often stay perfectly still when approached, just swivelling its eyes to assess the intruder. The varied habitat of the shallow waters in which they live give sea scorpions plenty of opportunity to show off their colour mimicry repertoire of pinks (encrusting algae), deep reds and browns (seaweeds) and oranges (sponges). These pages show some good examples of this chameleon-like activity, although the fish in the final photograph is included because it seems to have lost the plot. The claws and legs protruding from the corners of its mouth may be the explanation. In the act of grabbing or attempting to swallow the crab, it has moved from another position and apparently forgotten (or simply not had time) to blend in! The sea scorpion is in fact a voracious predator, creeping up on crustaceans or fish and then lurching forward to take them in a single gulp. Surprisingly large prey can be taken in the wide mouth. Like a number of bottom-living fish, sea scorpions lack a swimbladder to provide buoyancy and this explains their rather ungainly movements. Breeding takes place in the spring and clusters of orange eggs are laid in rock crevices or amongst

Long-spined sea scorpion - *Taurulus bubalis*

seaweeds. A very similar species, the short-spined sea scorpion (*Myoxocephalus scorpius*) is generally larger but less frequently encountered. Also known as the father lasher or bull rout, the spines on its gill covers are all of similar length and it lacks the mouth barbels of the long-spined sea scorpion. [Long-spined sea scorpion up to 20 cm long, short-spined up to 30 cm]

Orange to match sponge

Maroon to match seaweed

Distracted by food, too busy to change colour

Lumpsucker - *Cyclopterus lumpus*

Male with eggs (both photographs)

This strange fish has the least graceful appearance imaginable. Its stockily built body is rounded and humped, and the head is massive and very wide. It is protected by bony plates which form rows of bumps running along the length of the body. Colouration is bluish, greyish or greenish, the male taking on a reddish belly or flanks in the breeding season. There are two dorsal fins, but the foremost fin becomes overgrown by thick skin with age. The pelvic fins are fused to form a powerful sucker on the underside, just behind the chin, which is used for clinging onto rock surfaces. Lumpsuckers spend most of their time in fairly deep water but, between February and May, pairs meet up in shallow water where the female lays her eggs in a mass on a rocky ledge. She immediately returns to deeper water but the male stays to take care of the eggs for the one or two months until they hatch. It is during this time that most lumpsuckers are seen. The devoted father can keep scavenging animals away, but his chief duty may well be to keep the eggs oxygenated. He achieves this by fanning them with his fins or by pushing his head into the mass; the indentations caused by this action can sometimes be spotted. Any eggs that become rotten may also be eaten in order to keep the rest healthy. Egg masses are often laid in very shallow water, sometimes above low water mark, so wave surge could cause a real problem for the attendant male if he lacked the help of his sucker. The two photographs on this page show a male lumpsucker guarding a pale yellow egg mass near Brixham in April. [Females up to 60 cm long, males up to 50 cm]

Pogge (or hooknose) - *Agonus cataphractus*

An odd but unobtrusive fish usually found on sand or mud, the pogge has a head and body completely covered with keeled, bony plates. The underside of the wide but pointed head is covered with a beard-like array of barbels, and a pair of heavy curved spines on the snout gives the impression of an upturned nose. The pectoral fins are large but, behind them, the body tapers away to a very slim tail stem. Overall colour is greyish-brown with darker patches. The pogge appears to rely on its armour and camouflage for defence; the one shown here was quite willing to be gently manoeuvred into a position where a photograph was possible. [Up to 20 cm long but usually smaller]

Grey gurnard - *Eutrigla gurnardus*

Gurnards are another group of fish whose head is armoured with bony plates, but they have an unusual profile created by a very steep forehead. Their pectoral fins are also distinctive, with the foremost three rays separated from the rest of the fin to form "fingers" which probe for food and can "walk" the fish across the sea bed. The grey gurnard is mainly a greyish or reddish brown with numerous small pale blotches and an off-white underside. A dark blotch is often visible on the foremost dorsal fin. Other very similar gurnard species are distinguished by brilliant blue markings on the pectoral fins (tub gurnard, *Trigla lucerna*) or an overall red colour (red gurnard, *Aspitrigla cuculus*). [Up to 45 cm long]

Lesser sand eel - *Ammodytes tobianus*

Usually seen in dense shoals in sandy areas, particularly where there are also weed-covered rocks. They are very thin, silvery fish with a jutting lower jaw and forked tail fin. Shoals can swim very quickly, however, and all that may be seen is a swirling group of silvery streaks. Some of their time is spent buried in sand and an entire shoal can disappear into the sea bed in seconds. Conversely, a hand put down on the sea floor can cause a shoal to erupt into the open, a startling experience for the unwary. Shoals may be seen being followed by larger sand eel-shaped fish, which are probably greater sand eels (*Hyperoplus lanceolatus*) that feed on their smaller relatives. Sand eels form a major food source for many fish and sea birds. [Lesser up to 20 cm long, greater sand eel to 30 cm]

Bass - *Dicentrarchus labrax*

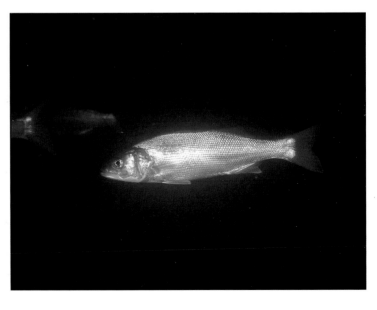

Bass are free swimmers, normally seen in small shoals in shallow rocky areas. They are more thick-set than fish such as pollack, and have much larger heads and mouths than grey mullet, but still appear very streamlined. The flanks are bright silver with the back slightly darker. Bass have a distinctly menacing look, and give the entirely accurate impression of being fast and voracious hunters. When found lurking near a wreck or reef, they will usually disappear immediately. A shoal may occasionally circle a stationary diver at a distance however, with a curious individual or two swooping down to take a closer look. [Up to 80 cm long]

Red mullet - *Mullus surmuletus*

The most distinctive features of this attractive fish are the pair of long feelers or barbels on its chin and the steep sloping forehead. The scales on its body are very obvious and the colour varies from yellow-brown to orange red, usually with pretty stripes or patterning. Red mullet can be seen "snuffling" around on sandy or muddy sea beds, using their barbels to feel for small buried animals on which they feed (see photograph). They are common in many sandy bays, often occurring in small groups. If a group is approached too closely, an individual fish raising its front dorsal fin seems to act as a signal for all the mullet to swim off. [Up to 40 cm long but usually much smaller]

Thick-lipped grey mullet - *Chelon labrosus*

Grey mullet are common but very shy fish. Divers or snorkellers can see them very close to stony beaches, sometimes in shoals, but one often gets only the most fleeting of glimpses as they disappear rapidly when approached. Groups of small individuals are found in rock pools. The grey to silvery body is torpedo-shaped with fairly distinct stripes down the flanks. If not scared off, grey mullet can be watched grazing head-down on the sea bed, scraping algae off stones and rocks or sucking up mud to extract any edible matter. The intestine is very long in order to handle this austere diet. There are two other similar species, the thin-lipped and golden grey mullets. [Up to 70 cm long]

Cuckoo wrasse - *Labrus bimaculatus*

Male

Female

The colourful wrasse are some of the most frequently seen fish in the West Country's coastal waters. Individuals of most of the five common species will be seen on virtually every dive, particularly in the summer months. The cuckoo wrasse may not be the most abundant of them, but its magnificent colouration and unusual behaviour tend to make it the most notable. An inquisitive and territorial male (top photograph) will often swim up to a diver's mask and look them straight in the eye before following them at close quarters, even taking the odd nibble on occasion. Males have a brilliant blue head with further blue markings interspersed with orange or yellow down the flanks. All cuckoo wrasse start life as females. Females are a coral pink with a distinctive row of black and white blotches along the rear of the back (smaller photograph). Some females turn into males later in life, depending on the proportion of the sexes in the local population. Individuals at an intermediate stage between female and male colouration will sometimes be seen. The cuckoo wrasse is usually restricted to slightly deeper water than the other wrasse species, so is seen less often when diving from the shore. [Males up to 35 cm long, females usually smaller]

Ballan wrasse - *Labrus bergylta*

The ballan is the largest of our wrasse, and has the appearance of being more heavily-built than the other slimmer species. Colouration is extremely variable, with many shades of brown, grey, green and red being found. There may be strong saddle-type markings, a mottled pattern or a single light stripe running the length of the body. Each of the large scales is usually relatively pale in the middle, and darker round the edge, which can give the whole fish a very spotty appearance. The young ballans, found in very shallow water and amongst seaweed in rock pools, are usually a vibrant emerald green. Like its close relative the cuckoo wrasse, the ballan always starts off life as a female but some individuals become males later in life, usually after several years of breeding as a female. Unlike the cuckoo however, ballan wrasse show no obvious colour change to mark their change of sex. One can only presume it must be obvious to other ballan wrasse! Most populations have many more females than males. The ballan is abundant in most rocky areas, from very shallow water down to 20 metres depth or so. It uses its strong front teeth to prise encrusting molluscs or barnacles from the rocks and also has additional teeth in the throat for crushing its food. When accompanied by rock cooks, I have seen it take in mouthfuls of gravel (see overleaf). Along with many fish species, the ballan wrasse is seen much less frequently out and about in shallow water during the winter. At this time however, small groups of individuals can often be found hiding in narrow rocky crevices. [Up to 50 cm long]

Rock cook - *Centrolabrus exoletus*

The rock cook is sometimes the forgotten species in descriptions of the wrasse, but it is very abundant in the South West and will often be seen in groups around a reef or piece of wreckage. Broadly similar in appearance to the other small wrasse, rock cooks are usually a pale reddish-brown with blue lines running along the side of the head; in the summer males have additional blue colouring down their back and flanks. The best distinguishing mark, however, is the broad dark band across the tail fin. The most notable feature of rock cook behaviour is their intriguing relationship with ballan wrasse. Rock cooks act as cleaner fish on the larger wrasse and will remove parasites from their flanks. Small groups of rock cooks can sometimes be seen escorting a single ballan, appearing to take turns in darting forward to have a quick nibble (top photograph, opposite page). Certain locations, such as the boilers on a shallow-water wreck, seem to serve as "cleaning stations" where this behaviour can regularly be observed. In some areas, particularly where patches of gravel intersperse the rocks around which the wrasse congregate, the two species also seem to feed together. A ballan hunting in the gravel for food may be surrounded by its little cohort of rock cooks looking for any scraps that are stirred up (bottom photograph, opposite page). The ballan will sometimes take a mouthful of small stones and spit them out, the rock cooks dashing in to examine material that starts to float away. [Up to 15 cm long]

Rock cook - *Centrolabrus exoletus*

Rock cook cleaning ballan wrasse

Rock cooks feeding with ballan wrasse

Goldsinny - *Ctenolabrus rupestris*

This small and slim wrasse lacks the colour and pattern variations displayed by most of its relatives, and so it is easier to identify. As the name suggests, the general colouration is a pinky or reddish brown akin to gold. The belly is paler and there may be faint stripes along the flanks. Aside from the colour, a reliable distinguishing feature is the large black spot located on the top side of the tail stem. The goldsinny's overall body shape is slightly different from that of the other wrasse species, being more torpedo-shaped. It swims in the typical manner common to all the wrasse however, usually keeping its body fairly stiff and using a rowing motion of the pectoral fins for propulsion. It can be very common in rocky areas, especially around underwater cliffs or rocky drop-offs, but is less abundant in the shallowest waters of the seaweed zone than the rock cook and corkwing. Goldsinnies will often approach divers quite closely, swimming to and fro in front of them but darting for cover if they make any sudden movements. They seem very inquisitive and I have often noticed them swimming round my head, gazing intently at my air bubbles while I take photographs. When observed closely, the protruding points of their outer row of teeth can be seen. These teeth enable goldsinnies to feed on encrusting organisms, as well as small crustaceans and other bottom-living animals [Up to 20 cm long]

Corkwing wrasse - *Crenilabrus melops*

Male with nest

The corkwing is another small and very abundant wrasse. It can be found in very shallow water, and the young are common in rock pools low down on the shore. The body is quite deep when viewed in profile, but rather slim when seen head-on. Distinguishing features include stripes on the cheeks, a dark blotch in the shape of a comma behind each eye and a dark spot in the middle of the tail stem (the latter can be very difficult to see). The overall colour is variable with females generally a pale brown, and males a darker more greenish brown, with hints of blue or dark red. Breeding males have superb colouration with brilliant blue or green mixed with claret, and very prominent cheek stripes. In the spring and early summer, male corkwings can be watched bustling around the rocks collecting scraps of seaweed in their mouths, which they then ram into a crevice to create a nest. Males invite females in to lay their eggs using a courtship display, and may try their luck with more than one female. Females with eggs can be recognised by the blue egg-laying papilla (protuberance) near the anal fin. After laying, the female has no more parental involvement but the male, once he has fertilised the eggs and put more seaweed over them, guards the nest. When engaged in building or guarding activities, the normally shy corkwing becomes bold and will attempt to ward off any approach to the nest. On occasion, they seem to swim away from the nest in full view and then return surreptitiously beneath the nearby kelp, as though attempting to mislead the potential predator. The photograph shows a male making adjustments to his nest. [Up to 25 cm long]

Tompot blenny - *Parablennius gattorugine*

Though usually small, tompot blennies are among the most charismatic fish seen in West Country waters. Their distinctive clown-like faces can frequently be seen peering out from crevices in reefs or wrecks, but they can also be found out in the open. The tompot blenny has a large mouth and eyes set high up on the head which, along with the large much-branched tentacle above each eye, contribute to the comical appearance. A much smaller fringed tentacle is positioned on the nostril beneath each eye. The elongated body is taller than it is broad, with a single dorsal fin that stretches almost back to the tail. The body's overall colour is a reddish or olive brown with several dark bands along its length. Like all blennies, tompots lack the buoyancy of a swimbladder and swim with a clumsy, though surprisingly rapid, wriggling motion. If the same site is dived regularly, a particular tompot may be spotted in the same hole on each visit. If the hole is empty, a short wait can result in the amusing sight of the resident bustling back into its home. Tompots are extremely inquisitive fish and may emerge from their shelter to take a closer look at the visiting diver. The odd individual may allow itself to be gently stroked, even appearing to become agitated when this is stopped. Tompot blennies will sometimes rush from their hiding place to see off other blennies or an intruding velvet swimming crab. They possess a single row of sharp teeth in each jaw and eat a variety of animals from the sea bed, including sea anemones which are unpalatable to most predators. Very small tompots can be found on the shore. [Up to 30 cm long but usually much smaller]

Tompot blenny - *Parablennius gattorugine*

Shanny - *Lipophrys pholis*

The shanny, occasionally known as the common blenny, is a fish of the shore and shallow water, usually seen in rock pools or by divers at the beginning or end of a beach dive. As well as hiding under stones or in holes, it can be seen in the open on barnacle covered rocks where its mottled pale brown and green colouring provides excellent camouflage. The shanny can also change colour to match its surroundings. It is very similar in shape to the tompot, but is usually smaller and lacks any head tentacles. It is more timid than the tompot and, when approached, it may carefully watch the viewer for just a few seconds before darting into a rock crack or under some seaweed. The two species have similar parenting arrangements, with the male guarding the eggs for a month or more until they hatch. During breeding and nesting, the male shanny's colours darken to almost black while the lips are a contrasting white. Shannies are omnivorous, eating seaweed as well as small animals such as worms and shrimps. They can sometimes be watched attempting to nip off the feeding limbs of barnacles as these sweep out to catch food. A shanny may live for as long as sixteen years. [Up to 15 cm long]

Black-face blenny - *Tripterygion delaisi*

Black-face blennies are quite rare but can be seen time and again in particular locations. They can be found regularly in a rocky gully near Wembury in South Devon for instance (where this one was photographed) and Portland is another favoured spot. They will often rest upside-down, underneath an overhang. Females are a drab mottled brown

while males are more colourful and have distinct black heads in the breeding season. Some of the fins bear an attractive sky-blue edging. Unlike the true blennies which have slippery skin and a single long dorsal fin, this fish has scales and three dorsal fins. [Up to 7 cm long]

Butterfish (or gunnel) - *Pholis gunnellus*

The eel-shaped butterfish, named after its slippery skin, is distinguished by the row of white-edged black spots along the base of its dorsal fin. Not a true blenny, but a close relative. Butterfish are found in crevices or creeping around the base of kelp plants, sometimes lifting their heads, snake-like, to get a better view. Their eggs are laid between December and March, in rock cavities or

empty mollusc shells in shallow water. Butterfish are very unusual in that both parents may take turns to guard the eggs (in most blennies and similar fish it is just the male). They curl their bodies around the eggs and prevent them from being scattered. [Up to 25 cm long]

Black goby - *Gobius niger*

Gobies are very abundant small fish, occasionally confused with blennies. Unlike blennies which tend to move with a wriggle, gobies have swimbladders and swim with a more graceful darting movement. They also possess two dorsal fins to the blennies' one. The black goby, common on sea beds of sand and mud, is larger and stouter than most gobies. Not really black, it is found in various shades of brown with darker blotches. There is a black mark at the front corner of both dorsal fins and the foremost fin is quite triangular

in shape. Gobies have similar breeding habits to blennies, with the male taking on egg-guarding duties. [Up to 17 cm long]

Rock goby - *Gobius paganellus*

Another fairly stout goby, this species is found on rocky ground as the name implies. It is common in rock pools on the shore, and divers will often see it peering out from a crevice or hole. The front dorsal fin has a pale band along its top edge, which can be red or orange in adult males. A further distinguishing feature

Goby eating a prawn

is the tiny branched tentacle by each nostril, though this is usually only seen when close-up photographs are examined after a dive. The fish in this photograph has just swallowed a surprisingly large prawn, and its tail can be seen protruding from the goby's mouth. [Up to 12 cm long]

Two-spot goby - *Gobiusculus flavescens*

The two-spot goby is reddish brown, with a paler underside and pretty pale blue markings along the sides of its body. There is a conspicuous black spot at the base of the tail fin, and males have another dark spot on their sides just behind the pectoral fin, hence the name. Two-spot gobies do not rest on the bottom for much of the time like other gobies, but dart continually around in the water a few inches above the sea bed, often in patches of seaweed. This habit, more than its markings, makes the species easy to identify. They are usually found in small groups that can sometimes be watched being tracked by predators such as young pollack. [Up to 6 cm long]

Painted goby - *Pomatoschistus pictus*

Gobies scavenging around a feeding crab

Several types of slim fawn gobies are seen darting across sandy sea beds. The painted goby can be recognised by its dorsal fins that are decorated by one or two rows of black spots. Reddish bands above the spots are especially developed in breeding males. The photograph shows a number of painted gobies darting expectantly around a feeding crab (page 29), hoping for any scraps. Divers disturbing the sand will also get the same attention because they may uncover small worms or shrimps. Two closely related species, the common goby (*P. microps*) and the sand goby (*P. minutus*) have no obvious spots on their dorsal fins but are very difficult to tell apart from each other. [All three *Pomatoschistus* species are rarely more than 6 cm long]

Leopard-spotted goby - *Thorogobius ephippiatus*

The attractive colouration of this splendid little fish makes it easier to identify than any of the other gobies. The overall body colour is a mauve-grey or fawn, and there are numerous dark brown or brick-red blotches all over the body and head, A fetching pale blue edging to the dorsal fins is sometimes visible. When studied closely, the outlines of the large diamond-shaped scales are also quite noticeable. Far from taking pride in their appearance, leopard-spotted gobies are extremely shy fish, disappearing into rocky crevices or the cavities beneath boulders at the first sign of attention. Escape is made even quicker by their tendency, while resting on the sea bed, to face towards their refuge. This attitude contrasts sharply with that of many other small fish, who seem keen to watch the world go by. Despite being so shy, leopard-spotted gobies are a very common sight when diving in rocky areas, particularly if a little sand or silt is present around the crevices. Before diving in such areas was commonplace, it was assumed to be a very rare species because so few were caught in trawls. [Up to 12 cm long]

Common dragonet - *Callionymus lyra*

A slender fish seen darting away on a sandy sea bed may well be a dragonet, but with this behaviour and the prominent eyes on top of the head, small specimens could be confused with gobies. The dragonet, however, has a much broader and nearly triangular head when seen from above. The snout is also much longer and incorporates a jutting lower jaw. Females and juvenile males are usually a pale, blotchy brown, sometimes with attractive mottling or patterns (top photograph). They are also capable of blending in perfectly with a coarse sand or gravel sea bed. The adult male is impressively coloured in hues of blue and yellow (bottom photograph) but is unfortunately a rare sight. Courtship apparently consists of the male performing an elaborate display, darting around in front of a female while spreading his brightly coloured fins and even pulling a strange face. Once the female is suitably impressed, they swim up towards the surface together and shed eggs and sperm into the water, their anal fins being positioned in such a way as to keep these together long enough for fertilisation to occur. Males are thought to only breed once in a

Female or juvenile male

Adult male

lifetime. Dragonets feed on small animals in the sand such as worms and crustaceans. Individual fish react differently when encountered, some disappearing rapidly while others seem content to be approached and photographed. [Females up to 20 cm long, males up to 30 cm]

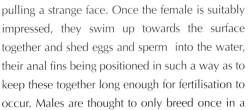

Plaice - *Pleuronectes platessa*

A common flatfish, frequently found on sandy and muddy sea beds, or on the sand patches that are interspersed with kelp-covered reefs in so many shallow-water areas of the West Country. Plaice are easily identified by the distinctive orange spots scattered over the upper side of their body. The background colour is usually grey-brown but this can change to blend in with the sea bed; the underside is a pearly white. Flatfish such as plaice are of course actually lying on their sides. Newly hatched from the floating egg, tiny flatfish look like conventional fish with the body positioned vertically in the water and an eye on either side. As they develop, still in open water, the body prepares itself for the bottom-living life. By the time the young fish have settled on the sea bed, one eye has moved over to join the other eye on the same side of the body, thus producing the typically twisted facial expression of all flatfish. Plaice are "right-eyed" in that the eyes both end up on what was originally the fish's right side. Female plaice lay up to half a million eggs at a time. Mating is not intimate as eggs and sperm are simply released into the water, but the female takes care to release her buoyant eggs beneath the male so they float up through his sperm to maximise fertilisation. Plaice are usually seen only when stationary, but prey on animals such as cockles, shrimps, worms and brittle stars while cruising over the sea bed. [Up to 90 cm long but usually no more than 50 cm]

Sole - *Solea solea*

The sole has a very characteristic rounded head, with a small curved mouth that is not positioned at the end of the snout as in most other flatfish. Its colour can vary from an even grey to a blotchy brown, depending on the sea bed. The pectoral fin on its upper side, which has a black patch at

its tip, can be held erect while the sole buries itself in the sand; it may mimic the dorsal fin of the poisonous weever fish and so help to repel predators. Like the plaice, the sole's eyes are on what started out as the right-hand side of its body. [Up to 40 cm long]

Topknot - *Zeugopterus punctatus*

The topknot is an unusual flatfish in that it is always found on rocky ground, unlike most species which are commonest on sand or mud. It is often seen in crevices, where it may lie flat against the ceiling. Its blotchy markings provide very effective camouflage and only its rippling fins or eyes glinting in a torch beam might

give it away. It has a broad body with a fringing dorsal fin that starts right next to the snout. Unlike most flatfish (such as plaice and sole) topknot are "left-eyed" so both eyes end up on what was originally the left side of the young fish. [Up to 25 cm long]

More information

The following publications were consulted during the writing of this book. I would recommend all of them for further reading.

Alexander, R. McN. (1990). Animals. Cambridge University Press.

Angel, H. (1975). Seashore Life on Sandy Beaches. Jarrold.

Boycott, B. B. (1958). The Cuttlefish - *Sepia*. In: New Biology, volume 25. Penguin.

Buchsbaum, R., Buchsbaum, M., Pearse, J. & Pearse, V. (1987). Animals Without Backbones, third edition. The University of Chicago Press.

Burton, M. & Burton, R. (1975). Encyclopedia of Fish. Octopus Books.

Daly, S. (1998). Marine Life of the Channel Islands. Kingdom Books.

Dipper, F. (1987). British Sea Fishes. Underwater World Publications.

Erwin, D. & Picton, B. (1987). Guide to Inshore Marine Life. Immel Publishing.

Fish, J. D. & Fish, S. (1996). A Student's Guide to the Seashore, second edition. Cambridge University Press.

Hanlon, R. T. & Messenger, J. B. (1988). Adaptive colouration in young cuttlefish: the morphology and development of body patterns and their relation to behaviour. Philosophical Transactions of the Royal Society. B, 320, 437-487.

Hayward, P. J. & Ryland, J. S. (1990). The Marine Fauna of the British Isles and North-West Europe. Oxford University Press.

Ingle, R. W. (1980). British Crabs. Oxford University Press.

Irving, R. (1998). Sussex Marine Life, an Identification Guide for Divers. East Sussex County Council.

Kershaw, D. R. (1988). Animal Diversity. Chapman & Hall.

Lythgoe, J. & Lythgoe, G. (1971). Fishes of the Sea. Blandford Press.

Muus, B. J. & Dahlstrom, P. (1974). The Sea Fishes of Britain and North-Western Europe. Collins.

Picton, B. E. (1993). A Field Guide to the Shallow-water Echinoderms of the British Isles. Immel Publishing.

Picton, B. E. & Morrow, C. C. (1994). A Field Guide to the Nudibranchs of the British Isles. Immel Publishing.

Thompson, T. E. (1976). Biology of Opisthobranch Molluscs. The Ray Society.

Thompson, T. E. (1988). Molluscs: Benthic Opisthobranchs. The Linnean Society.

Warner, G. F. (1977). The Biology of Crabs. Paul Elek (Scientific Books).

Wood, E. (1988). Sea Life of Britain and Ireland. Immel Publishing.

Yonge, C. M. (1949). The Sea Shore. Collins.

Yonge, C. M. & Thompson T. E. (1976). Living Marine Molluscs. Collins.

More action

In addition to reading more, what else can you do to learn about our marine animals and help with their conservation? With respect to both of these aims, I would like to recommend the following organisations:

The Marine Conservation Society is the UK's foremost charity dedicated to the protection of our seas and marine wildlife. They work through campaigning, education and persuasion, always based on sound research. They aim to involve people in the care and protection of the sea and its wildlife and can be reached at: 9 Gloucester Road, Ross-on-Wye, Herefordshire, HR9 5BU.

The National Marine Aquarium, in Plymouth, is a charity dedicated to increasing awareness and understanding of the oceans; the life they contain and man's interaction with them. Their aim is to entertain visitors while imparting an appreciation of water and the life it supports, through a series of stunning displays. They are at: Rope Walk, Coxside, Plymouth, Devon, PL4 0LF.